Algebra
FOR
DUMMIES®
PORTABLE EDITION

by Mary Jane Sterling

WILEY

Wiley Publishing, Inc.

Algebra For Dummies®, Portable Edition

Published by
Wiley Publishing, Inc.
111 River St.
Hoboken, NJ 07030-5774
www.wiley.com

For general information on our other products and services, please contact our Customer Care Department within the U.S. at 800-762-2974, outside the U.S. at 317-572-3993, or fax 317-572-4002.

For technical support, please visit www.wiley.com/techsupport.

Wiley also publishes its books in a variety of electronic formats. Some content that appears in print may not be available in electronic books.

Library of Congress Control Number: 2006923913

ISBN-13: 978-0-470-05377-5

ISBN-10: 0-470-05377-1

Manufactured in the United States of America

10 9 8 7 6 5 4 3 2 1

1B/SS/QV/QW/IN

WILEY

About the Author

Mary Jane Sterling has been an educator since graduating from college. Teaching at the junior high, high school, and college levels, she has had the full span of experiences and opportunities while working in education. She has been teaching at Bradley University in Peoria, Illinois, for the past twenty years.

Publisher's Acknowledgments

We're proud of this book; please send us your comments through our Dummies online registration form located at www.dummies.com/register/.

Some of the people who helped bring this book to market include the following:

Acquisitions, Editorial, and Media Development

Project Editor: Tracy Barr

Acquisitions Editor: Kathy Cox

Editorial Program Coordinator: Hanna K. Scott

Editorial Manager: Michelle Hacker

Editorial Supervisor: Carmen Krikorian

Editorial Assistants: Nadine Bell, Erin Calligan, David Lutton

Cover Photos: Getty Images

Cartoons: Rich Tennant (www.the5thwave.com)

Composition Services

Project Coordinator: Kristie Rees

Layout and Graphics: Denny Hager, Heather Ryan, Erin Zeltner

Proofreaders: Laura Albert, Laura L. Bowman, Jessica Kramer

Indexer: Joan Griffitts

Publishing and Editorial for Consumer Dummies

Diane Graves Steele, Vice President and Publisher, Consumer Dummies

Joyce Pepple, Acquisitions Director, Consumer Dummies

Kristin A. Cocks, Product Development Director, Consumer Dummies

Michael Spring, Vice President and Publisher, Travel

Kelly Regan, Editorial Director, Travel

Publishing for Technology Dummies

Andy Cummings, Vice President and Publisher, Dummies Technology/ General User

Composition Services

Gerry Fahey, Vice President of Production Services

Debbie Stailey, Director of Composition Services

Contents at a Glance

Table of Contents

Introduction

● ●

*O*ne of the most commonly asked questions in a mathematics classroom is, "What will I ever use algebra for?" Some teachers can give a good, convincing answer. Others hem and haw and stare at the floor. My favorite answer is, "Algebra gives you power." Algebra gives you the power to move on to bigger and better things in mathematics. Algebra gives you the power of knowing something that your neighbor doesn't know. Algebra gives you the power to be able to help someone else with an algebra task or to explain to a friend about these logical mathematical processes. Algebra is a system of symbols and rules that is universally understood, no matter what the spoken language. Algebra provides a clear, methodical process that can be followed from beginning to end. It's an organizational tool that is most useful when followed with the appropriate rules. What power!

About This Book

If you're looking for help with some of the basic tools of algebra, you can find that type of information in this book. Think of these tools as being like what a cook needs. You can't cook a soufflé unless you know how to whisk the eggs and turn on the oven. Your success later depends on your preparation. Of course, you may be beyond these basics. I also spend a lot of time explaining factoring. Factoring is really no more than changing what the expression looks like. And the factored form is one where everything is all multiplied together. You can find which of the factoring techniques you need to brush up on if you get stuck with a problem. I also give you simple equations and the rules and methods you need to solve them.

Following the conventions

You find two ways of expressing numbers or numerals: In the descriptions, math operators (plus sign, equal signs, and so on) are spelled out. In problems and examples, though, I use the actual symbols. This should make for an easier read.

Terms special to algebra are italicized and defined.

Eyeing those icons

The silly little drawings in the margin of the book are there to draw your attention to specific text. The icons I use in this book include the following:

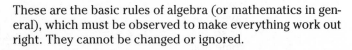

These are the basic rules of algebra (or mathematics in general), which must be observed to make everything work out right. They cannot be changed or ignored.

These paragraphs, often attached to sidebars, offer facts you may find interesting, but that you do not need to know. These tidbits are absolutely not important, but they make algebra a little less impersonal and ethereal.

These paragraphs help clarify a symbol or process, a technical term, or an expression. I may discuss the topic in another section of the book, or just be reminding you of a basic algebra rule.

The info next to this icon isn't life-or-death important, but it generally can help make your life easier — at least your life in algebra.

This alerts you to something that can be particularly tricky. Errors crop up frequently when working with the process or topic next to this icon, so I call special attention to these problem spots with this icon.

What Not to Read

You can get a lot from this book by just going from icon to icon. The text next to the Algebra Rules icons pull everything together very tidily. It's when you want more detail that you want to read between the icons.

The sidebars (those little gray boxes) include some historical stuff — mathematicians' lives may not make for exciting movies, but some mathematicians have done some rather interesting things. There are also some of my favorite anecdotes and stories to lighten the mood. You can pick and choose rather easily because of the general format.

Foolish Assumptions

I'm not going to assume that you're as crazy about math as I am — you may be even more excited about it! I do assume, though, that you have a mission here — to brush up on your skills, improve your mind, or just have some fun. I also assume that you have some experience with algebra — full exposure for a year or so, maybe a class you took a long time ago, or even just some preliminary concepts.

Where to Go from Here

You can go anywhere you like from here. Head to the Table of Contents to find a chapter that sounds interesting, peruse the index for a list of individual topics, or begin in Chapter 1 and move through sequentially. Wherever you go, you can't go wrong. So welcome to algebra! Enjoy the adventure!

Chapter 1

Assembling Your Tools

*Y*ou probably have heard the word *algebra* on many occa-
sions and knew that it had something to do with mathematics. Perhaps you know enough to know that algebra has
enough information to require taking two separate high school
algebra classes — Algebra I and Algebra II. But what exactly is
algebra? What is it really used for?

This chapter answers these questions and more, providing
the straight scoop on some of the contributions to algebra's
development, what it's good for, how algebra is used, and
what tools you need to make it happen.

What Algebra Does

In a nutshell, algebra is a way of generalizing arithmetic.
Through the use of variables that can generally represent any
value in a given formula, general formulas can be applied to
all numbers. Algebra uses positive and negative numbers,
integers, fractions, operations, and symbols to analyze the
relationships between values. It's a systematic study of numbers and their relationship, and it uses specific rules.

For example, the formula $a \times 0 = 0$ shows that any real number, represented here by the a, multiplied by zero, always equals zero.

In algebra, by using an x to represent the number two, for example, in $x + x + x = 6$, you can generalize with the formula $3x = 6$.

You may be thinking, "That's great and all, but come on. Is it really necessary to do that — to plop in letters in place of numbers and stuff?" Well, yes. Early mathematicians found that using letters to represent quantities simplified problems. In fact, that's what algebra is all about — simplifying problems.

The basic purpose of algebra has been the same for thousands of years: to allow people to solve problems with unknown answers.

Beginning with the Basics: Numbers

Where would mathematics and algebra be without numbers? A part of everyday life, numbers are the basic building blocks of algebra. Numbers give you a value to work with.

Even the simple tasks and the most common of circumstances require a knowledge of numbers. Suppose that you wanted to figure the amount of gasoline it takes to get from home to work and back each day. You need a number for the total miles between your home and business and another number for the total miles your car can run on one gallon of gasoline.

The different sets of numbers are important because what they look like and how they behave can set the scene for particular situations or help to solve particular problems. It's sometimes really convenient to declare, "I'm only going to look at whole-number answers," because whole numbers do not include fractions. This may happen if you're working through a problem that involves a number of cars. Who wants half a car?

Algebra uses different sets of numbers, such as whole numbers and those that follow, to solve different problems.

Really real numbers

Real numbers are just what the name implies. In contrast to imaginary numbers, they represent real values — no pretend or make-believe. Real numbers, the most inclusive set of numbers, comprise the full spectrum of numbers; they cover the gamut and can take on any form — fractions or whole numbers, decimal points or no decimal points. The full range of real numbers includes decimals that can go on forever and ever without end. The variations on the theme are endless.

For the purposes of this book, I always refer to real numbers.

Counting on natural numbers

A natural number is a number that comes naturally. What numbers did you first use? Remember someone asking, "How old are you?" You proudly held up four fingers and said, "Four!" The natural numbers are also counting numbers: 1, 2, 3, 4, 5, 6, 7, and so on into infinity.

You use natural numbers to count items. Sometimes the task is to count how many people there are. A half-person won't be considered (and it's a rather grisly thought). You use natural numbers to make lists.

Wholly whole numbers

Whole numbers aren't a whole lot different from the natural numbers. The whole numbers are just all the natural numbers plus a zero: 0, 1, 2, 3, 4, 5, and so on into infinity.

Whole numbers act like natural numbers and are used when whole amounts (no fractions) are required. Zero can also indicate none. Algebraic problems often require you to round the answer to the nearest whole number. This makes perfect sense when the problem involves people, cars, animals, houses, or anything that shouldn't be cut into pieces.

Integrating integers

Integers allow you to broaden your horizons a bit. Integers incorporate all the qualities of whole numbers and their opposites, or *additive inverses* of the whole numbers (refer to the "Operating with opposites" section in this chapter for information on additive inverses). Integers can be described as being positive and negative whole numbers: . . ., –3, –2, –1, 0, 1, 2, 3, ...

Integers are popular in algebra. When you solve a long, complicated problem and come up with an integer, you can be joyous because your answer is probably right. After all, it's not a fraction! This doesn't mean that answers in algebra can't be fractions or decimals. It's just that most textbooks and reference books try to stick with nice answers to increase the comfort level and avoid confusion. This is the plan in this book, too. After all, who wants a messy answer, even though, in real life, that's more often the case.

Being reasonable: Rational numbers

Rational numbers act rationally! What does that mean? In this case, acting rationally means that the decimal equivalent of the rational number behaves. The decimal ends somewhere, or it has a repeating pattern to it. That's what constitutes "behaving." In other words, the decimal doesn't go on. Examples inlcude 2, 3.4, 5.77623, –4.5. Other rational numbers have decimals that repeat the same pattern, such as $3.164164164\ldots = 3.\overline{164}$, or $.666666666\ldots = .\overline{6}$. The horizontal bar over the 164 and the 6 lets you know that these numbers repeat forever.

In all cases, rational numbers can be written as a fraction. They all have a fraction that they are equal to. So one definition of a rational number is any number that can be written as a fraction.

Digits, fingers, and toes through history

The main reason humans developed a decimal, or base-ten, system is because humans usually have ten fingers and ten toes. It could have been a base-twenty system or a base-five system — like the Babylonians had. From about 1700 B.C. until about A.D. 500, however, most scientists used a base-sixty system. Using sixty as a base came about because the number of days in a year was estimated to be roughly 360 days, and sixty was one of the nice divisors of 360. Remnants of the early base-sixty system are found in our minutes and seconds. Can you imagine having to remember sixty different digits instead of just ten?

Restraining irrational numbers

Irrational numbers are just what you may expect from their name — the opposite of rational numbers. An *irrational number* cannot be written as a fraction, and decimal values for irrationals never end and never have a nice pattern to them. Whew! Talk about irrational! For example, pi, with its never-ending decimal places, is irrational.

Evening out even and odd numbers

An *even number* is one that divides evenly by two. "Two, four, six, eight. Who do we appreciate?"

An *odd number* is one that does not divide evenly by two. The even and odd numbers alternate when you list all the integers.

Varying Variables

Algebra uses letters, called *variables*, to represent numbers that correspond to specific values. Usually, if you see letters toward the beginning of the alphabet in a problem, such as *a, b,* or *c,* they represent known or set values, and the letters toward the end of the alphabet, such as x, y, or z, represent the unknowns, things that can change, or what you're solving for.

Variable is the most general word for a letter that represents the unknown, or what you're solving for in an algebra problem. A variable always represents a number.

The following list goes through some of the more commonly used variables.

- ✔ An n doesn't really fall at the beginning or end of the alphabet, but it's used frequently in algebra, often representing some unknown quantity or number — probably because n is the first letter in number.

- ✔ The letter x is often the variable you solve for, maybe because it's a letter of mystery: X marks the spot, the x-factor, *The X Files*. Whatever the reason x is so popular as a variable, the letter also is used to indicate multiplication. You have to be clear, when you use an x, that it isn't taken to mean multiply.

- ✔ C and k are two of the more popular letters used for representing known amounts or constants. The letters that represent variables and numbers are usually small case: a, b, c, and so on. Capitalized letters are used most commonly to represent the answer in a formula, such as the capital A for area of a circle equals pi times the radius squared, $A = \pi r^2$. The letter C, mentioned previously as being a popular choice for a constant, is used frequently in calculus and physics, and it's capitalized there — probably more due to tradition than any good reason.

Speaking in Algebra

Algebra and symbols in algebra are like a foreign language. They all mean something and can be translated back and forth as needed. It's important to know the vocabulary in a foreign language; it's just as important in algebra.

- ✔ An *expression* is any combination of values and operations that can be used to show how things belong together and compare to one another. $2x^2 + 4x$ is an example of an expression.

✔ A *term*, such as 4*xy,* is a grouping together of one or more factors (variables and/or numbers). Multiplication is the only thing connecting the number with the variables. Addition and subtraction, on the other hand, separate terms from one another. For example, the expression 3*xy* + 5*x* – 6 has three terms.

✔ An *equation* uses a sign to show a relationship — that two things are equal. By using an equation, tough problems can be reduced to easier problems and simpler answers. An example of an equation is $2x^2 + 4x$.

✔ An *operation* is an action performed upon one or two numbers to produce a resulting number. Operations are addition, subtraction, multiplication, division, square roots, and so on. See Chapter 6 for more on operations.

✔ A *variable* is a letter that always represents a number, but it varies until it's written in an equation or inequality. (An inequality is a comparison of two values.) Then the fate of the variable is set — it can be solved for, and its value becomes the solution of the equation.

✔ A *constant* is a value or number that never changes in an equation — it's constantly the same. Five (5) is a constant because it is what it is. A variable can be a constant if it is assigned a definite value. Usually, a variable representing a constant is one of the first letters in the alphabet. In the equation $ax^2 + bx + c,$ *a, b,* and *c* are constants and the *x* is the variable. The value of *x* depends on what *a, b,* and *c* are assigned to be.

✔ An *exponent* is a small number written slightly above and to the right of a variable or number, such as the 2 in the expression 3^2. It's used to show repeated multiplication. An exponent is also called the *power* of the value. For more on exponents, see Chapter 4.

Taking Aim at Algebra Operations

In algebra today, a variable represents the unknown (see more on variables in the "Speaking in Algebra" section, earlier in this chapter). Before the use of symbols caught on, problems were written out in long, wordy expressions. Actually, using signs and operations was a huge breakthrough. First, a few operations were used, and then algebra became fully symbolic. Nowadays, you may see some words alongside the operations to explain and help you understand, like having subtitles in a movie. Look at this example to see what I mean. Which of the following would you rather write out?

> The number of quarts of water multiplied by six and then that value added to three

or

$6x + 3$

I'd go for the second option. Wouldn't you?

Deciphering the symbols

The basics of algebra involve symbols. Algebra uses symbols for quantities, operations, relations, or grouping. The symbols are shorthand and are much more efficient than writing out the words or meanings. But you need to know what the symbols represent, and the following list shares some of that info.

- ✔ + means add or find the sum, more than, or increased by; the result of addition is the sum.

- ✔ – means subtract or minus or decreased by or less; the result is the difference.

- ✔ × means multiply or times. The values being multiplied together are the multipliers or factors; the result is the product. Some other symbols meaning multiply can be grouping symbols: ( ), [ ], { }, *. In algebra, the × symbol is used infrequently because it can be confused with the variable *x*. The dot (·) is popular because it's easy to write. The grouping symbols are used when you need to contain many terms or a messy expression. By themselves, the grouping symbols don't mean to multiply, but if you put a value in front of a grouping symbol, it means to multiply. For more on the grouping symbols, skip ahead to the "Grouping" section.

- ✔ ÷ means divide. The number that's going into the dividend is the divisor. The result is the quotient. Other signs that indicate division are the fraction line and slash, /.

✔ √ means to take the square root of something — to find the number, which multiplied by itself gives you the number under the sign (see more on square roots in Chapter 4).

✔ | | means to find the absolute value of a number, which is the number itself or its distance from zero on the number line (see more on absolute value in Chapter 2).

✔ . . . means et cetera, and so on, or in the same pattern. You use an ellipsis in algebra when you have a long list of numbers and don't want to have to write all of them. For instance, if you want to list numbers starting with 1 and going up by 1 forever and ever, write: 1, 2, 3, 4, ... Or you can write the list of numbers from 600 through 1,000 as, 600, 601, 602, . . . , 1,000.

✔ π is the Greek letter pi that refers to the irrational number: 3.14159 . . . . It represents the relationship between the diameter and circumference of a circle.

Grouping

Grouping symbols tell you that you have to deal with the terms inside the grouping symbols before you deal with the larger problem.

The main grouping symbols are

✔ ( ) Parentheses (This one is used most often.)

✔ [ ] Brackets

✔ { } Braces

The beginning of the equal sign

Robert Recorde first used the equal sign (=) in the mid-1500s. He wrote, "I will sette as I doe often in woorke use, a paire of parrallels, or Gemowe lines of one lengthe, thus ==, because noe 2 thynges can be moare equalle." However, not all mathematicians immediately accepted the equal sign. Some preferred two upright parallel lines. A symbol resembling α (with longer "tails") was also popular for quite a while. The equal sign seemed to have been generally accepted in the mid-1600s.

For example, 8 – (4 – 2) says to do what's in the parentheses first. This is different from (8 – 4) – 2. The first expression works out to be 6, and the second expression to 2.

These three grouping symbols — the parentheses, brackets, and braces — are used both alone and with each other. When used together, the symbols organize a more complicated problem.

Defining relationships

Algebra is all about relationships — not the he-loves-me-he-loves-me-not kind of relationship, but the relationships between numbers or among the terms of an equation. Although algebraic relationships can be just as complicated as romantic ones, you have a better chance of understanding an algebraic relationship. The symbols for the relationships are given here:

- ✔ = means that the first value is equal to or the same as the value that follows.

- ✔ ≠ means that the first value is not equal to the value that follows.

- ✔ ≈ means that one value is approximately the same or about the same as the value that follows; this is used when rounding numbers.

- ✔ ≤ means that the first value is less than or equal to the value that follows.

- ✔ < means that the first value is less than the value that follows.

- ✔ ≥ means that the first value is greater than or equal to the value that follows.

- ✔ > means that the first value is greater than the value that follows.

Operating with opposites

When solving equations in algebra, doing the opposite to work your way toward the answer comes up often. You have to undo operations that have been done to the variable. The opposite of an operation is another operation that gets you back where you started. This is used primarily to get rid of numbers that are combined with a variable so you can solve for the variable in an equation.

Being contrary: Doing opposite operations

The opposite of adding 3 is subtracting 3. If you add 3 to 100, you get 103. If you then subtract 3 from 103, you're back where you started.

- The opposite of addition is subtraction.
- The opposite of subtraction is addition.
- The opposite of multiplication is division.
- The opposite of division is multiplication.
- The opposite of taking a square root is *squaring* (multiplying a value by itself).
- The opposite of squaring is taking the square root.
- The opposite of cubing is taking the cube root.

Dealing with the opposites of numbers

A number actually has two opposites: the additive inverse and the multiplicative inverse.

- The *additive inverse* is the number with the opposite sign. So –3 is the additive inverse of 3, and 16 is the additive inverse of –16. Use these if 3 or 16 is being added to a variable, and you want to get the variable alone; this is used when solving an equation for the value of the variable.

- The *multiplicative inverse* is also called the *reciprocal*. The reciprocal is the original number written as the bottom of a fraction with a one on the top. So $\frac{1}{2}$ is the reciprocal of 2, and 25 is the reciprocal of $\frac{1}{25}$. If a number starts out as a fraction, its reciprocal is just that number written upside-down. So the reciprocal of $\frac{4}{7}$ is $\frac{7}{4}$. Use this if a number multiplies or divides a variable; it gets the variable alone so it can be solved for.

Playing by the Rules

The basics of algebra involve rules, like the rules to follow when you're driving. If everyone follows the same rules, accidents and chaos are less likely. The same goes for algebra. You have to observe the rules of algebra when you work with variables, numbers, and symbols. Following the rules is especially important when you solve problems because you don't know what number a variable stands for. So in algebra, you simplify, factor, solve, and check.

- ✔ To *simplify* means to combine all that can be combined, cut down on the number of terms, and put an expression in an easily understandable form.

- ✔ To *factor* means to change two or more terms to just one term.

- ✔ *Solve* means to find the answer. In algebra, it means to figure out what the variable stands for.

Algebra involves symbols, such as variables and operation signs, which are the tools that you can use to make algebraic expressions more useable and readable. These things go hand in hand with simplifying, factoring, and solving problems, which are easier to solve if broken down into basic parts. Using symbols is actually much easier than wading through a bunch of words.

Chapter 2

Assigning Signs: Positive and Negative Numbers

*N*umbers have many characteristics: They can be big, little, even, odd, whole, fraction, positive, negative, and sometimes cold and indifferent — I'm kidding about that last one. Chapter 1 describes numbers' different names and categories. But this chapter concentrates on just the positive and negative characteristics.

Positive and *negative* are words you use and hear every day:

> "You have a positive influence on me."

> "I'm getting negative vibes."

This chapter tells you how to add, subtract, multiply, and divide signed numbers, no matter whether all the numbers are the same sign or mixed-and-matched.

Showing Some Signs

Early on, mathematicians realized that using plus and minus signs and making rules for their use was going to be a big advantage in their number world. They also realized that if they used the minus sign, there was no need to create a bunch of completely new symbols for negative numbers. After all, positive and negative numbers are related to one another, and the slight addition of the minus sign works well. Negative numbers have positive counterparts and vice versa. This means that –3 and +3 are related. A new symbol, such as a ∝, didn't have to be created to represent the opposite of three — they could just use the minus sign. If you have a handle on what having six bananas would be like, then you can imagine what *not* having six bananas would be like, also.

Numbers that are opposite in sign but the same otherwise are *additive inverses*.

Two numbers are additive inverses of one another if their sum is zero, $a + (-a) = 0$. Additive inverses are always the same distance from zero (in opposite directions) on the number line. For example, the additive inverse of –6 is +6; the additive inverse of $+\frac{1}{5}$ is $-\frac{1}{5}$.

Picking out positive numbers

Positive numbers are bigger, greater, or higher than zero. They are on the opposite side of zero from the negative numbers. If you arrange a tug-of-war between positive and negative numbers, the positive numbers line up on the right side of zero, as Figure 2-1 shows.

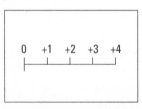

Figure 2-1: Some positive numbers all lined up.

Positive numbers get bigger and bigger the farther they are from zero: 81 is bigger than 25 because it's farther away from zero; 212° F, the boiling temperature of water, is farther away from zero than 32° F, the temperature at which water freezes.

They're both positive numbers, but one may seem more positive than the other. Check out the difference between freezing water and boiling water to see how much more positive a number can be!

Making the most of negative numbers

The concept of a number less than zero can be difficult to grasp. Sure you can say "less than zero," and even write a book with that title, but what does it really mean? Think of entering the ground floor of a large government building. You go to the elevator and have to choose between going up to the first, second, third, or fourth floors, or going down to the first, second, third, fourth, or fifth subbasement (down where all the secret stuff is). The farther you are from the ground floor, the farther the number of that floor is from zero. The second subbasement could be called floor –2, but that may not be a good number for a floor.

Negative numbers are smaller than zero. On a line with zero in the middle, negative numbers line up on the left, as shown in Figure 2-2.

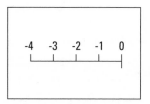

Figure 2-2: Negative numbers lining up on the left.

Negative numbers get smaller and smaller the farther they are from zero. This can get confusing because you may think that –400 is *bigger* than –12. But just think of –400° F and –12° F. Neither is anything pleasant to think about, but –400° is definitely less pleasant — colder, lower, smaller.

Regarding negative numbers, the number closer to zero is the *bigger* number.

Comparing positives and negatives

Although my mom always told me not to compare myself to other people, comparing numbers to other numbers is often useful. And, when you compare numbers, the greater-than (>) and less-than (<) signs come in handy, which is why I use them in Table 2-1, where I put some positive and negative signed numbers in perspective.

Table 2-1   Comparing Positive and Negative Numbers

Comparison	What It Means
6 < 2	2 is less than 6; 2 is closer to 0 than 6 is.
10 > 0	10 is greater than 0; 10 is positive and is bigger than 0.
−5 > −8	−5 is greater than −8; −5 is closer to 0 than −8 is.
−300 > −400	−300 is larger than −400.
0 > −6	−6 is negative and is smaller than 0.
7 > −80	Positive numbers are always bigger than negative numbers.

So, putting the numbers 6, −2, −18, 3, 16, and −11 in order from smallest to biggest gives you: −18, −11, −2, 3, 6, and 16, which are shown as dots on a number line in Figure 2-3.

Plus (+) and minus (−) signs

The first time plus (+) and minus (−) signs appeared in print, they referred to surpluses and deficits in business situations — not to arithmetic operations. But even before these signs appeared formally in print, the plus and minus symbols were used extensively. For example, plus and minus signs were painted on barrels of goods to indicate whether the barrels were full or not.

TECHNICAL STUFF

Negatives

Early Chinese civilizations were responsible for many important inventions and discoveries. The Chinese are credited with developing gun powder, printing, paper, and the compass. They also had a good way to deal with negative numbers — long before negative numbers were formally recognized.

The Chinese used two sets of calculating rods — a red set for positive coefficients and a black set for negative coefficients. For some reason, the colors were eventually reversed, and now red indicates a financial deficit or negative (such as "in the red") and black means to the good or positive.

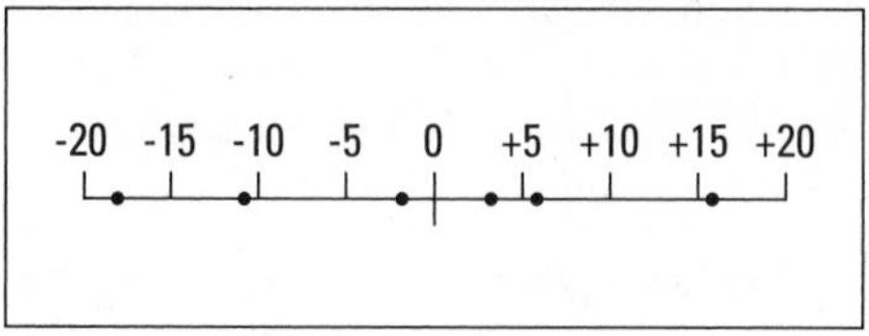

Figure 2-3: Positive and negative numbers on a number line.

Zeroing in on zero

But what about zero? I keep comparing numbers to see how far they are from zero. Is zero positive or negative? The answer is that it's neither. Zero has the unique distinction of being neither positive nor negative. Zero separates the positive numbers from the negative ones — what a job!

Going In for Operations

Operations in algebra are nothing like operations in hospitals. Well, you get to dissect things in both, but dissecting numbers is a whole lot easier (and a lot less messy) than dissecting things in a hospital.

Algebra is just a way of generalizing arithmetic, so the operations and rules used in arithmetic work the same for algebra.

Some new operations crop up, though, to make things more interesting than just adding, subtracting, multiplying, and dividing. I'm going to introduce one of those new operations after explaining the difference between a binary operation and a nonbinary operation.

Breaking in to binary operations

Relax, I haven't suddenly switched to *Astronomy For Dummies.* The *binary* in this section refers to operations with two numbers, not systems with two stars.

Bi means two. A *bi*cycle has two wheels. A *bi*gamist has two spouses. A *bi*nary operation involves two numbers. Addition, subtraction, multiplication, and division are all *binary operations* because you need two numbers to perform them. You can add 3 + 4, but you can't add 3 + if there's nothing after the plus sign. You need another number.

Introducing nonbinary operations

A *nonbinary operation* needs just one number. A nonbinary operation performs a task and spits out the answer. Square roots are nonbinary operations. You find the square root of 4 by performing this operation on just one number. See Chapter 4 for more on square roots.

One of the most important nonbinary operations is finding the absolute value of a number. The *absolute value* operation tells you how far a number is from zero. It doesn't pay any attention to whether the number is less than or greater than zero; it just determines *how far* it is from zero.

The symbol for absolute value is two vertical bars: | |.

The absolute value of *a,* where *a* represents any real number, either positive or negative, is

  ✔ $|a| = a$, where $a \geq 0$.

  ✔ $|a| = -a$, where $a \geq$ (negative), and $-a$ is positive.

TECHNICAL STUFF

Making your own binary operation

All it takes to create a binary operation is to make up a rule as to how it works and what numbers can be used. For example, you could say, "I have a new binary operation named star, *. When you star two numbers together, you put a 0 between them." For example, 4*7 = 407. As you can see 4*7 is not the same as 7*4.

Now, you may say, what good is this operation? None that I can see. Maybe this gives you more of an appreciation for the binary operations that already exist. They do something useful.

Doing absolute value operations looks like this:

$$|3| = 3$$
$$|-4| = 4$$
$$|-87| = 87$$
$$|0| = |0|$$

Basically, the absolute value operation tells you how far the number is from zero. It doesn't pay any attention to whether the number is less than zero or greater than zero; it just determines *how far* from zero.

Operating with Signed Numbers

If you're on an elevator in a building with four floors above the ground floor and five floors below ground level, you can have a grand time riding the elevator all day, pushing buttons, and actually "operating" with signed numbers. You're probably too young to remember this, but people actually used to get paid to ride elevators and push buttons all day. I wonder if these people had to understand algebra first. If you want to go up five floors from the third subbasement, you end up on the second floor above ground level.

Adding like to like: Same-signed numbers

When your first grade teacher taught you that one plus one equals two, she probably didn't tell you that this was just one part of the whole big addition story. She didn't mention that adding one positive number to another positive number is really a special case. If she *had* told you this big story stuff — that you can add positive and negative numbers together or add any combination of positive and negative numbers together — you might have packed up your little school bag and sack lunch and left the room right then and there.

Adding all positive numbers is just a small part of the whole addition story, but it was enough to get you started at that time. This section gives you the big story — all the information you need to add signed numbers.

The first thing to consider in adding signed numbers is to start with the easiest situation: The numbers have the same sign. Look at what happens:

✔ You have 3 apples and your friend gives you 4 apples.

$$(+3) + (+4) = +7$$

You now have 7 apples.

✔ You owed Jon $8 and had to borrow $2 more.

$$(-8) + (-2) = -10$$

Now you're $10 in debt.

There's a nice "S" rule for this addition. See if you can say it quickly three times in a row: When the signs are the same, you find the sum, and the sign of the sum is the same as the signs.

This rule holds when a and b represent any two real numbers:

$$(+a) + (+b) = +(a + b)$$
$$(-a) + (-b) = -(a + b)$$

I wish I had something as alliterative for all the rules, but this is math — not poetry!

Say you're adding –3 and –2. The signs are the same; so you find the sum of 3 and 2, which is 5. The sign of this sum is the same as the signs of –3 and –2, so the *sum* is also a negative.

Check out these examples:

> ✔ (+8) + (+11) = +19. The signs are all positive.
>
> ✔ (–14) + (–100) = –114. The sign of the sum is the same as the signs.
>
> ✔ (+4) + (+7) + (+2) = +13. Because all the numbers are positive, add them and make the sum positive, also.
>
> ✔ (–5) + (–2) + (–3) + (–1) = –11. This time all the numbers are negative, so add them and give the sum a minus sign.

Adding same-signed numbers is a snap! (A little more alliteration for you.)

Adding different signs

Can a relationship between a Leo and a Gemini ever add up to anything? I don't know the answer to that question, but I do know that numbers with different signs add up very nicely. You just have to know how to do it, and in this section, I tell you.

When the signs of two numbers are different, forget the signs for a while and find the difference between the numbers. This is the difference between their absolute values. (For a refresher on absolute values, turn to the "Introducing nonbinary operations" section, earlier in this chapter.) The number farther from zero determines the sign of the answer.

$$(+a) + (-b) = +(|a| - |b|) \text{ if the positive } a \text{ is farther from zero.}$$

$$(+a) + (-b) = -(|b| - |a|) \text{ if the negative } b \text{ is farther from zero.}$$

Look what happens when you add numbers with different signs:

✔ You had $20 in your wallet and spent $12 for your theatre ticket.

$$(+20) + (-12) = +8$$

After settling up, you have $8 left.

✔ I have $20, but it costs $32 to fill my car's gas tank.

$$(+20) + (-32) = -12$$

I'll have to borrow $12 to fill the tank.

The following examples give you some more combinations:

✔ $(+6) + (-7) = -1$. The difference between 6 and 7 is 1. Seven is farther from 0 than 6 is, so the answer is –1.

✔ $(-6) + (+7) = +1$. This time the 7 is positive. It's still farther from 0 than the 6. The answer this time is +1.

✔ $(-4) + (+3) + (+7) + (-5) = +1$. If you take these in order from left to right (although you can add in any order you like), you add the first two together to get –1. Add that to the next to get +6. Then add this to the last number to get +1.

Subtracting signed numbers

Subtracting signed numbers is really easy to do: You _don't!_ Instead of inventing a new set of rules for subtracting signed numbers, mathematicians determined that it's easier to change the subtraction problems to addition problems and use the rules I explained in the previous section.

Think about that for a moment. Just change the subtraction problem into an addition problem. It doesn't make much sense, does it? Everybody knows that you can't just change an arithmetic operation and expect to get the same or right answer. You found out a long time ago that 10 – 4 isn't the same as 10 + 4. You can't just change the operation and expect it to work out correctly.

So to make this work, you really change _two_ things to even things out.

Coming up with nothing

Consider adding two numbers with different signs where there is no difference between the absolute value of the numbers:

$$(+3) + (-3)$$

$$(-5) + (+5)$$

The difference between the numbers without their signs is zero. And because zero is neither positive nor negative — it has no sign — that takes care of having to determine what the sign of the answer is by which is farther from zero. Neither wins! So, in the following examples, zero is the hero:

$$(-10) + (+10) = 0$$

$$(-a) + (+a) = 0$$

$$(+abc) + (-abc) = 0$$

In the last two examples, assume that a, b, and c are the same throughout the expression.

When subtracting signed numbers, change the minus sign to a plus sign *and* change the number that the minus sign was in front of to its opposite. Then just add the numbers using the rules for adding signed numbers. See Chapter 1 for more on opposites.

✔ $(+a) - (+b) = (+a) + (-b)$

✔ $(+a) - (-b) = (+a) + (+b)$

✔ $(-a) - (+b) = (-a) + (-b)$

✔ $(-a) - (-b) = (-a) + (+b)$

The following examples put these concepts into real-life terms:

✔ The submarine was 60 feet below the surface when the skipper shouted, "Dive!" It went down another 40 feet.

$$-60 - (+40) = -60 + (-40) = -100$$

Change from subtraction to addition. Change the 40 to its opposite, –40. Then use the addition rule. The submarine is now 100 feet below the surface.

✔ Kids play a version of "Mother may I?" where players may ask, "Mother, may I take three steps forward?" A "Yes" answer allows the player to move three steps closer to Mother. A "No" answer means the player takes three steps backward. A player may ask, "Mother, may I take four steps backward?" In this case, a "No" answer means take four steps forward. The net result of these two answers is

$$(-3) - (-4) = (-3) + (+4) = +1$$

Change the –4 to its opposite to change from subtraction to addition. The player is one step closer to Mother after the two moves.

To subtract signed numbers, change the minus sign to a plus sign and change the sign of the number that follows.

Multiplying and dividing signed numbers

Multiplication and division are really the easiest operations to do with signed numbers. As long as you can multiply and divide, the rules are not only simple, but they're also the same for both operations.

When multiplying and dividing two signed numbers, if the two signs are the same, then the result is *positive;* when the two signs are different, then the result is *negative:*

$$(+a) \times (+b) = +ab \qquad (+a) \div (+b) = +(a \div b)$$
$$(+a) \times (-b) = -ab \qquad (+a) \div (-b) = -(a \div b)$$
$$(-a) \times (+b) = -ab \qquad (-a) \div (+b) = -(a \div b)$$
$$(-a) \times (-b) = +ab \qquad (-a) \div (-b) = +(a \div b)$$

Notice in which cases the answer is positive and in which cases it's negative. Also, notice that multiplication and division seem to be "as usual" except for the positive and negative signs. Check out the following examples:

✔ $(-8) \times (+2) = -16$

✔ $(-5) \times (-11) = +55$

✔ $(+24) \div (-3) = -8$

✔ $(-30) \div (-2) = +15$

You can mix up these operations doing several multiplications or divisions or a mixture of each and using the following Even-Odd Rule.

Even-Odd Rule: When multiplying and dividing a bunch of numbers, count the number of negatives to determine the final sign. An *even* number of negatives means the result is *positive*. An *odd* number of negatives means the result is *negative*. The following examples show you how it's done:

✔ $(+2) \times (-3) \times (+4) = -24$: This problem has just one negative sign. Because one is an odd number (and often the loneliest number), the answer is negative.

✔ $(+2) \times (-3) \times (+4) \times (-1) = +24$: Two negative signs mean a positive answer because two is an even number.

✔ $\dfrac{(+4) \times (-3)}{(-2)} = +6$: An even number of negatives means a positive answer.

✔ $\dfrac{(-12) \times (-6)}{(-4) \times (+3)} = -6$: Three negatives yield a negative.

✔ $(-1)(-1)(-1)(-1)(-1)(-1)(-1)(-1)(-1)(-1)(-1)(-1)(-1)(-1)(-1) = -1$: An odd number of negative signs gives you a negative answer.

Finally, you can prove to your mother that sometimes two wrongs *do* make a right!

Working with Nothing: Zero and Signed Numbers

What role does zero play in the signed number show? What does it do to the signs of the answers? Well, when you're doing addition or subtraction, what zero does depends on where it is. When you multiply or divide, zero tends to just wipe out the numbers and leave you with zero.

Some general guidelines about zero:

✔ **Adding zero:** $0 + a$ is just a. Zero doesn't change the value of a. (This is also true for $a + 0$.)

🖐 **Subtracting zero:** $0 - a = -a$. Use the rule for subtracting signed numbers: Change the operation from subtraction to addition and change the sign of the second number. Likewise, $a - 0 = a$. It doesn't change the value of a to subtract zero from it.

🖐 **Multiplying by zero:** $a \times 0 = 0$. If you're in a club with a bunch of friends and none of you has anything, multiplying what each of you has yields nothing: Likewise, $0 \times a = 0$.

Multiplying any number by zero always yields zero.

🖐 **Dividing by zero:** $0 \div a = 0$. Take you and your friends: If none of you has anything, dividing that *nothing* into shares just means that each share has nothing. And you can't use zero as the divisor because if you have a things, you can't divide them into zero parts.

So, working with zero isn't too tricky. You follow normal addition and subtraction rules, and just keep in mind that multiplying and dividing with zero leaves you with nothing — literally.

Associating and Commuting with Expressions

Algebra operations follow certain rules, and those rules have certain properties. In this section, I talk about two of those properties — the commutative property and the associative property.

Reordering operations: The commutative property

Before discussing the commutative property, take a look at the word *commute*. You probably commute to work or school and know that whether you're going from home to work or from work to home, the distance is the same: The distance doesn't change because you change directions (although getting home during rush hour may make that distance *seem* longer).

The same principle is true of *some* algebraic operations: It doesn't matter whether you add $1 + 2$ or $2 + 1$; the answer is still 3. Likewise, multiplying 2×3 or 3×2 yields 6.

The *commutative property* means that you can change the order of the numbers in an operation without affecting the result. Addition and multiplication are commutative. Subtraction and division are not. So,

$$a + b = b + a$$

$$a \times b = b \times a$$

$$a - b \neq b - a \text{ (except in a few special cases)}$$

$$a \div b \neq b \div a \text{ (except in a few special cases)}$$

In general, subtraction and division are *not* commutative. The special cases occur when you choose the numbers carefully. For instance, if *a* and *b* are the same number, then the subtraction appears to be commutative because switching the order doesn't change the answer. In the case of division, if *a* and *b* are opposites, then you get −1 no matter which order you divide them in. This is why, in mathematics, big deals are made about proofs. A few special cases of something may work, but a real rule or theorem has to work all the time.

Look at the following examples:

- 4 + 5 = 9 and 5 + 4 = 9, so 4 + 5 = 5 + 4.

- $3 \times (-7) = -21$ and $(-7) \times 3 = -21$, so $3 \times (-7) = (-7) \times 3$.

- $(-5) - (+2) = (-7)$ and $(+2) - (-5) = +7$, so $(-5) - (+2) \neq (+2) - (-5)$.

- $(-6) \div (+1) = -6$ and $(+1) \div (-6) = -\frac{1}{6}$, so $(-6) \div (+1) \neq (+1) \div (-6)$.

Keep in mind that the commutative property holds true only for addition and multiplication.

Associating expressions: The associative property

The commutative property has to do with the order of the numbers when you perform an operation. The associative property has to do with how the numbers are grouped when you perform an operation on more than two numbers.

Think about what the word *associate* means. When you associate with someone, you're close to the person, or you form a group with the person. Say that Anika, Becky, and Cora associate. Whether Anika drives over to pick up Becky and the two of them go to Cora's and pick her up, or Cora is at Becky's house and Anika picks up both of them at the same time, the same result occurs — the same people are in the car at the end.

The *associative property* means that if the grouping of the operation changes, the result remains the same. (If you need a reminder about grouping, check out Chapter 1.) Addition and multiplication are associative. Subtraction and division are *not* associative operations. So,

$$a + (b + c) = (a + b) + c$$
$$a \times (b \times c) = (a \times b) \times c$$
$$a - (b - c) \neq (a - b) - c \text{ (except in a few special cases)}$$
$$a \div (b \div c) \neq (a \div b) \div c \text{ (except in a few special cases)}$$

You can always find a few cases where the property works even though it isn't supposed to. For instance, in the subtraction problem $5 - (4 - 0) = (5 - 4) - 0$, the property seems to work. Also, in the division problem $6 \div (3 \div 1) = (6 \div 3) \div 1$, it seems to work. Although there are exceptions, a rule must work *all* the time.

Some real-number examples may make this clearer:

✔ $4 + (5 + 8) = 4 + 13 = 17$ and $(4 + 5) + 8 = 9 + 8 = 17$, so $4 + (5 + 8) = (4 + 5) + 8$.

✔ $3 \times (2 \times 5) = 3 \times 10 = 30$ and $(3 \times 2) \times 5 = 6 \times 5 = 30$, so $3 \times (2 \times 5) = (3 \times 2) \times 5$.

✔ $13 - (8 - 2) = 13 - 6 = 7$ and $(13 - 8) - 2 = 5 - 2 = 3$, so $13 - (8 - 2) \neq (13 - 8) - 2$.

✔ $48 \div (16 \div 2) = 48 \div 8 = 6$ and $(48 \div 16) \div 2 = 3 \div 2 = \frac{3}{2}$, so $48 \div (16 \div 2) \neq (48 \div 16) \div 2$.

The commutative and associative properties come in handy when you work with algebraic expressions. You can change the order of some numbers or change the grouping to make the work less messy or more convenient. Just keep in mind that you can commute and associate addition and multiplication operations, but not subtraction or division.

Chapter 3

Figuring Out Fractions and Dealing with Decimals

....

In This Chapter

▶ Fracturing whole numbers into decimals

▶ Changing how a fraction looks

▶ Practicing operations on fractions instead of people

▶ Dividing whole pies into pieces

....

*A*t one time or another, most math students wish that the world was made up of whole numbers only. But those non-whole numbers called fractions really make the world a wonderful place. (Well, that may be stretching it a bit.) In any case, fractions are here to stay, and this chapter helps you delve into them in all their wondrous workings.

This chapter gets down to the basics with the rules involving fractions so you can play the game. You may not think that decimals belong in a chapter on fractions, but there's no better place for them. Decimals are just shorthand for the most common fractions. Words that are often used are abbreviated, such as Mr., Dr., Tues., Oct., and so on! Likewise, fractions with denominators of 10, 100, 1,000, and so on are abbreviated with decimals.

Pulling Numbers Apart and Piecing Them Back Together

Understanding fractions, where they come from, and why they look the way they do helps when you're working with them. A fraction has two parts:

$$\frac{\text{top}}{\text{bottom}} \text{ or } \frac{\text{numerator}}{\text{denominator}}$$

The *denominator,* or bottom number, tells you the total number of items. The *numerator,* or top number, tells you how many of the total (the bottom number) are being considered.

Perhaps you can remember the exact placement of the numbers and their proper names if you think in terms of

- ✔ **N:** **N**umerator; **N**orth; ↑
- ✔ **D:** **D**enominator; **D**own; ↓

In all the cases using fractions, the denominator tells you how many equal portions or pieces there are. Without the equal rule, you could get different pieces in various sizes. For instance, in a recipe calling for $\frac{1}{2}$ cup of flour, if you didn't know that the one part was one of two equal parts, then there could be two unequal parts — one big and one little. Should the big or the little part go into the cookies?

Along with terminology like numerator and denominator, fractions fall into one of three types: proper, improper, and mixed, which are covered in the following sections.

Making your bow to proper fractions

The simplest type of fraction to picture is a *proper fraction,* which is always just part of one whole thing. One whole pie can be cut into proper fractions. One whole play can be divided into fractions — acts or scenes.

In a proper fraction, the numerator is always smaller than the denominator, and the fraction's value is always less than one.

Take a look at the following proper fractions:

- ✔ $\frac{5}{6}$: Cut a cake into six slices (six shows how many things equal the total).

  Eat one piece, and you still have five pieces left. Lucky you! You can have your cake and eat it too!

- ✔ $\frac{4}{12}$: You took four months out of last year to finish the project.

- ✔ $\frac{1}{16}$: One pound of butter equals 16 ounces. Put one ounce of butter on the popcorn.

Getting to know improper fractions

An *improper fraction* has more parts than necessary for one whole number, which has nothing to do with a lack of social decorum. These top-heavy fractions, however, are useful in many situations. The bottom number tells you what size the pieces are. It's just that in the case of improper fractions, there are more than enough pieces to make one whole number.

Improper fractions are fractions whose numerators, or tops, are bigger than their denominators.

- ✔ $\frac{15}{8}$: After the party, Maria put all the leftover pieces of pizza together. There were 15 pieces, each $\frac{1}{8}$ of a pizza.

- ✔ $\frac{4}{3}$: Quadrupling a recipe that calls for $\frac{1}{3}$ c. sugar requires four measures of sugar, each $\frac{1}{3}$ of a cup.

They may be called improper, but these fractions behave very well.

Mixing it up with mixed numbers

Improper fractions can get a bit awkward. Mixed numbers help clean up the act. Using a *mixed number* — one with both a whole number and a fraction — to express the same thing that an improper fraction expresses makes things easier to deal with. For example, instead of using the improper fraction $\frac{4}{3}$, you can use the mixed number $1\frac{1}{3}$. Recipes are easier to use; hat sizes are easier to read.

A *mixed number* contains both a whole number and a fraction, as the following examples show:

- $4\frac{1}{2}$: The recipe calls for four and one-half cups of flour.

- $7\frac{3}{8}$: The hat size is 7 plus $\frac{3}{8}$ more so it isn't too tight.

- $5\frac{7}{12}$: It's been 5 years and 7 months since he left for Europe.

Converting fractions on Wall Street

Stocks in the U.S. Stock Market used to be priced using fractions for the parts. You'd see prices, such as $16\frac{3}{4}$, and read that the price had gone down by $\frac{5}{8}$. This custom of using fractions is supposed to have started when coins could be broken into pieces; it's easier to break something in half, then the half into halves (quarters), then the quarters into halves (eighths), and so on.

In the year 2000, the stock market changed these parts to decimals. This wasn't any response to a desire to go metric. It was just to make the increments smaller. There are eight divisions between each number and the next if you use eighths and ten divisions using decimals, or tenths. The tenths are smaller than eighths, so there are smaller steps going up (or down).

Following the Sterling Low-Fraction Diet

When you use fractions, you want them to be as nice as possible. In this case, *nice* means the smallest possible numbers in the numerator and denominator of the fraction. Sometimes small numbers are just easier to deal with — easier to understand and easier to visualize — than larger numbers. Doing the arithmetic is much easier with smaller numbers, too.

A fraction is in lowest terms if no number (other than 1) divides both the numerator and denominator evenly.

Figuring out equivalent fractions

When you multiply or divide the numerator and denominator of a fraction by the same number, you don't change the value of the fraction. In fact, you're basically multiplying or dividing by one because any time the numerator and denominator of a fraction are the same number, it equals one. If you divide the numerator and denominator of $\frac{16}{32}$ by 4, you're basically dividing $\frac{16}{32}$ by $\frac{4}{4}$, which equals one.

- $\frac{4}{5}$ has the same value as $\frac{48}{60}$, which has the same value as $\frac{32}{40}$.

- $\frac{4}{5} = \frac{4 \times 12}{5 \times 12} = \frac{48}{60}$.

- $\frac{32}{40} = \frac{32 \div 8}{40 \div 8} = \frac{4}{5}$.

- $\frac{32}{40} = \frac{32 \times 1.5}{40 \times 1.5} = \frac{48}{60}$.

Not all fractions with large numbers, however, can be changed to smaller numbers. Certain rules have to be followed so that the fraction maintains its integrity; it has to have the same value as it did originally.

To reduce fractions to their lowest terms, follow these steps:

As an example, reduce $\frac{48}{60}$ to lowest terms.

1. **Look for numbers that evenly divide both the numerator and denominator.**

   In the example, 12 goes into both 48 and 60 evenly.

2. **Do the division.**

   $$\frac{48 \div 12}{60 \div 12} = \frac{4}{5}$$

3. **Plug the reduced fraction into your problem.**

   So, instead of working with $\frac{48}{60}$, you can work with $\frac{4}{5}$.

When can you use this reducing process? Well, what if you spent 48 minutes waiting in line to buy your airline ticket? That's 48 minutes out of the total 60 minutes in an hour. As a fraction, that's written $\frac{48}{60}$. You can see that 48 out of 60 is a big hunk of time. To get a better picture of what is going on, put the fraction in lowest terms: 12 divides both 48 and 60 evenly.

You spent $\frac{4}{5}$ of the hour standing in line.

Realizing why smaller is better

Why is $\frac{4}{5}$ better than $\frac{48}{60}$? Most people can relate better to smaller numbers. You can picture four out of five things in your mind more easily than you can picture 48 out of 60 — refer to Figure 3-1 if you don't believe me. A couple more examples may help you get this:

✔ A survey found that 162 out of 198 people preferred Bix Peanut Butter. The fraction $\frac{162}{198}$ reduces to $\frac{9}{11}$, which offers more information as far as the preference for the peanut butter.

✔ An ad on TV says, "Nine out of ten dentists surveyed prefer Squishy Toothpaste." I've always wondered how many dentists were actually surveyed. The fraction $\frac{9}{10}$ gives good information as far as the preference, but were only ten dentists surveyed or were a thousand?

Figure 3-1 is an illustration that makes a case for smaller being better. On the left, there are a total of sixty divisions. On the right, there are a total of five divisions.

- ✔ You paid 18 installments out of a total of 36 for a new television. Both numbers are divisible by 18 — 18 goes into 18 once (1), and 18 goes into 36 twice (2). So you know that you have made one-half, $\frac{1}{2}$, of your total payments. That's $\frac{18}{36} = \frac{18 \div 18}{36 \div 18} = \frac{1}{2}$

  You're half done or have half to go — depending on whether you're a glass-half-full or glass-half-empty personality.

- ✔ Your favorite pitcher has pitched 96 innings so far. Because there are 9 innings in a regulation game, he has pitched $\frac{96 \text{ innings}}{9 \text{ innings}}$ per game $= 10\frac{6}{9}$ games.

  Because $\frac{96}{9}$ is an improper fraction, first divide 96 by 9 and write the remainder as a fraction. $\frac{96}{9} = 10\frac{6}{9} = 10\frac{2}{3}$ games.

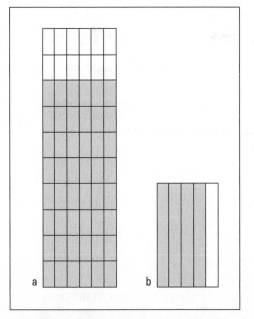

Figure 3-1: Forty-eight of sixty, or four of five? You decide.

A remainder is the value left over when one number is divided by another.

What to do when you can't go any lower

It's always nice when you can reduce a fraction to make it more user-friendly. The fraction $\frac{3}{4}$ is much nicer than $\frac{447}{596}$. Sometimes, though, the fraction just doesn't want to cooperate. You still have options: You can round up or down, and then you can multiply or divide by one.

Rounding up or down

Try reducing $\frac{25}{36}$ into its lowest terms. Twenty-five can be divided by 5 or 25, and 36 can be divided by 2, 3, 4, 6, 9, 12, 18, and 36, but none of these match with 5 or 25. Even though 25 and 36 are not prime numbers, they have no common factor. The fraction cannot be reduced.

In cases where the fraction won't reduce to lower terms, you can just leave well enough alone, or, if you're so inclined, round the numerator or denominator up or down to make it reducible.

For example, $\frac{301}{498}$ doesn't reduce. But, if you round the numerator down to 300 and the denominator up to 500, you get an approximate fraction $\frac{300}{500}$ that reduces to $\frac{3}{5}$. In this case, the rounding doesn't change the value by much. You just have to use your judgment.

Dividing by one

Any number divided by one equals that number: For any real number n,

$$n \div 1 = n$$

So, knowing this allows you to change how a fraction looks without changing its value. See how it works in the following example?

$$\frac{8}{12} \div 1 \text{ could be } \frac{8}{12} \div \frac{4}{4} = \frac{2}{3} = \frac{8}{12}$$

You do the same thing on the top and bottom of the fraction, so you really just divide by one, which doesn't change the value — just how it looks.

Multiplying by one

Any number multiplied by one equals that number: For any real number n,

$$n \times 1 = n$$

Like division, you can multiply by one and change how a fraction looks without changing its value. That is,

$$4 \times 1 = 4 \qquad -8 \cdot 1 = -8 \qquad \frac{3}{4} \times 1 = \frac{3}{4}$$

In the case of fractions, instead of actually using one, a fraction equal to one is used.

$$1 = \frac{3}{3} = \frac{7}{7} = \frac{10}{10} = \ldots$$

Using the fractional value for the number one allows you to change how fractions look without changing their value.

$$\frac{2}{3} \times 1 \text{ could be } \frac{2}{3} \times \frac{4}{4} = \frac{8}{12} = \frac{2}{3}$$

Table 3-1 lists some equivalent fractions of everyday things.

Table 3-1	Some Equivalent Fractions
Fractions	*Equivalent*
$\frac{1}{2} = \frac{2}{4} = \frac{3}{6} = \frac{4}{8} = \frac{5}{10}$	One half of a basketball game
$\frac{2}{3} = \frac{4}{6} = \frac{6}{9} = \frac{8}{12} = \frac{10}{15}$	Two periods of a hockey game
$\frac{4}{7} = \frac{8}{14} = \frac{12}{21} = \frac{16}{28} = \frac{20}{35}$	Four days of a week
$\frac{5}{9} = \frac{10}{18} = \frac{15}{27} = \frac{20}{36} = \frac{25}{45}$	Five innings of a baseball game

(continued)

Table 3-1 *(continued)*

Fractions	Equivalent
$\frac{7}{12} = \frac{14}{24} = \frac{21}{36} = \frac{28}{48} = \frac{35}{60}$	Seven months of a year
$\frac{23}{24} = \frac{46}{48} = \frac{69}{72} = \frac{92}{96} = \frac{115}{120}$	Twenty-three hours of a day

Fitting Fractions Together

To add, subtract, or compare fractions, you need fractions with the same number of equal pieces. In other words, the denominators have to be the same.

Finding common denominators

Common denominators, or the same numbers in the denominators, are necessary for adding, subtracting, and comparing fractions. Carefully selected fractions that equal the number one are used to create common denominators because multiplying by one doesn't change a number's value.

Follow these steps to find a common denominator for two fractions and write the equivalent fractions. Use the two fractions $\frac{7}{18}$ and $\frac{5}{24}$ as an example:

1. **Look to see if you can find a common denominator just by observation.**

   The numbers 18 and 24 are pretty big, and nothing jumps out at first. If you do find one, go down to Step 4.

2. **Determine which fraction has the larger denominator.**

   In this case the 24 is the larger of the two denominators.

3. **Check to see if the smaller denominator divides the larger one evenly. If not, check multiples of the larger denominator until you find one that the smaller denominator can divide into evenly, too.**

   The number 18 doesn't divide 24 evenly. Two times 24 is 48, but 18 doesn't divide that evenly, either. Three times 24 is 72. Eighteen does divide that evenly. The common denominator is 72.

4. **Write the two fractions as equivalent fractions with the common denominator.**

   The number 24 divides 72 three times, so the fraction $\frac{5}{24}$ is multiplied by $\frac{3}{3}$.

   $$\frac{5 \times 3}{24 \times 3} = \frac{15}{72}$$

   Eighteen divides 72 four times, so the fraction $\frac{7}{18}$ is multiplied by $\frac{4}{4}$.

   $$\frac{7 \times 4}{18 \times 4} = \frac{28}{72}$$

Now follow the same steps, using the two fractions $\frac{3}{8}$ and $\frac{5}{12}$ as an example:

1. **Find a common denominator.**

   The numbers 8 and 12 both have the number 24 as a multiple. If you see this right away, you can go to Step 4.

2. **Determine which fraction has the larger denominator.**

   In this case, the 12 is the larger of the two denominators.

3. **Check multiples.**

   Eight doesn't divide 12 evenly. Two times 12 is 24, and 8 does divide that evenly. The common denominator is 24.

4. **Write as equivalent fractions.**

   Twelve divides 24 two times, so the fraction $\frac{5}{12}$ is multiplied by $\frac{2}{2}$.

   $$\frac{5 \times 2}{12 \times 2} = \frac{10}{24}$$

   Eight divides 24 three times, so the fraction $\frac{3}{8}$ is multiplied by $\frac{3}{3}$.

   $$\frac{3 \times 3}{8 \times 3} = \frac{9}{24}$$

 Sometimes you can get a denominator that fits quickly by multiplying the two denominators together. This method doesn't always give the best or smallest choice, but it's efficient.

Find a common denominator for $\frac{5}{8}$ and $\frac{4}{9}$. Multiply the two denominators together, $8 \times 9 = 72$. Then you can see that you want:

✔ $\frac{5}{8} = \frac{?}{72}$ and $\frac{4}{9} = \frac{?}{72}$.

By multiplying the numerators by the same factors, you get:

$$\frac{5 \times 9}{8 \times 9} = \frac{45}{72} \text{ and } \frac{4 \times 8}{9 \times 8} = \frac{32}{72}.$$

✔ Find a common denominator for $\frac{3}{5}$ and $\frac{5}{12}$.

Multiply 5×12 to get a common denominator of 60.

$$\frac{3}{5} = \frac{36}{60} \text{ and } \frac{5}{12} = \frac{25}{60}.$$

Working with improper fractions

Multiplying and dividing improper fractions (see the "Getting to know improper fractions" section, earlier in this chapter, for an introduction) is no more difficult than multiplying or dividing other fractions. Understanding the final result is easier, however, if you write the answer as a mixed number (see the "Mixing it up with mixed numbers" section, earlier in this chapter).

To change an improper fraction to a mixed number, divide the numerator by the denominator. The number of times the denominator divides is the whole number in front, and the remainder — the leftover value — is written as a proper fraction, which has a numerator smaller than the denominator. See the similarity and difference between mixed numbers and improper fractions in the following examples:

✔ $\frac{11}{9} = 1\frac{2}{9}$: The number 9 divides 11 once with 2 left over.

✔ $\frac{26}{7} = 3\frac{5}{7}$: The number 7 divides 26 three times with 5 left over.

✔ $\frac{402}{11} = 36\frac{6}{11}$: Eleven divides 402 thirty-six times with 6 left over. This example makes it especially apparent that the mixed number is more understandable.

Putting Fractions to Task

Now that you know everything about fractions — their proper names, characteristics, strong and weak points, and so on — it's time to put them to work. The rules for addition, subtraction, multiplication, and division of fractions are the same ones used when variables are added. This is reassuring! The rules don't change.

Adding and subtracting fractions

Adding and subtracting fractions takes a little special care. You can add quarts and gallons if you change them to the same unit (quarts). It's the same with fractions. You can add thirds and sixths if you find the common denominator first.

To add or subtract fractions:

1. **Convert the fractions so that they have the same number in the denominators.**

   Find out how to do this in the "Finding common denominators" section.

2. **Add or subtract the numerators. Leave the denominators alone.**

3. **Reduce the answer, if needed.**

A question about an athlete named Jim can demonstrate:

✔ Jim played for half an hour in yesterday's soccer game and for 20 minutes in today's game. How long did Jim play altogether?

Set up a simple equation, such as $\frac{1}{2} + \frac{1}{3}$ = hours Jim played.

One-half and one-third don't fit together. You can't just add the numerators and the denominators because two-fifths doesn't make any sense. $\frac{1}{2} + \frac{1}{3}$ does not equal $\frac{2}{5}$. But, you realize that $\frac{1}{2}$ can also be $\frac{2}{4}, \frac{3}{6}, \frac{4}{8}, \frac{5}{10}$, or many other things, and $\frac{1}{3}$ can also be $\frac{2}{6}, \frac{3}{9}, \frac{4}{12}, \frac{5}{15}$, or many other things.

So, you can fit the two fractions together by multiplying both the numerators and the denominators by the same number: Multiply $\frac{1}{2}$ by $\frac{3}{3}$ to make $\frac{3}{6}$; multiply $\frac{1}{3}$ by $\frac{2}{2}$ to make $\frac{2}{6}$. $\left(\frac{3}{3} = 1 = \frac{2}{2}\right)$

Notice that $\frac{1}{2}$ and $\frac{1}{3}$ each can have a 6 for the denominator, so that they can fit together: $\frac{1}{2}$ and $\frac{1}{3}$ are equal to $\frac{3}{6}$ and $\frac{2}{6}$.

Now you can add the numerators $\frac{3}{6}$ and $\frac{2}{6}$.

Then solve the equation: $\frac{1}{2} + \frac{1}{3} = \frac{3}{6} + \frac{2}{6} = \frac{3+2}{6} = \frac{5}{6}$.

Jim played $\frac{5}{6}$ of an hour altogether.

Another real-life situation shows you how you can make fractions fit to do a simple subtraction.

✔ In her will, Jane gave $\frac{4}{7}$ of her money to the Humane Society and $\frac{1}{3}$ of her money to other charities. How much was left for her children's inheritance?

The fractions $\frac{4}{7}$ and $\frac{1}{3}$ aren't compatible. You can't combine or compare them. The fraction $\frac{4}{7}$ can be $\frac{8}{14}$ or $\frac{12}{21}$ or $\frac{16}{28}$, and more. The fraction $\frac{1}{3}$ can be $\frac{2}{6}, \frac{3}{9}, \frac{4}{12}, \frac{5}{15}, \frac{6}{18}, \frac{7}{21}$, and more.

It may take a while to find a good fit, but $\frac{4}{7} = \frac{12}{21}$ and $\frac{1}{3} = \frac{7}{21}$.

Add the numerators to get the total designation to charity in Jane's will.

$$\frac{12}{21} + \frac{7}{21} = \frac{19}{21}$$

Subtract that total from the whole of Jane's proceeds to find what portion is allotted to her children.

$$\frac{21}{21} - \frac{19}{21} = \frac{2}{21}$$

Jane's children will be awarded $\frac{2}{21}$ of Jane's estate.

Multiplying fractions

Multiplying fractions is a tad easier than adding or subtracting them. This is because you don't need to find a common denominator first. The only catch is that you have to change any mixed numbers to improper fractions. Then, at the end, you may have to change the fraction back again to a mixed number.

When multiplying fractions, follow these steps:

1. **Change all mixed numbers to improper fractions.**

2. **Multiply the numerators together and the denominators together.**

3. **Reduce the answer if necessary.**

Fred and Sadie's stories offer opportunities to multiply fractions:

✔ Fred ate $\frac{2}{3}$ of a $\frac{3}{4}$-pound box of candy. How much candy did he eat?

$\frac{2}{3} \times \frac{3}{4} = \frac{6}{12} = \frac{1}{2}$ pound of candy (and 6 zillion calories).

✔ Sadie worked $10\frac{2}{3}$ hours at time-and-a-half. How many hours will she get paid for?

$10\frac{2}{3} \times 1\frac{1}{2} = \frac{32}{3} \times \frac{3}{2} = \frac{96}{6} = 16$ earned hours to multiply by the hourly rate.

Reducing the fractions before multiplying can make multiplying fractions easier. Smaller numbers are more manageable, and if you reduce the fractions before you multiply, you don't have to reduce them afterwards.

This is another way of looking at Fred's candy problem:

✔ The expression $\frac{2}{3} \times \frac{3}{4}$ has a 2 in the first numerator and a 4 in the second denominator. Even though they aren't in the same fraction, this is a multiplication problem. Multiplication is *commutative,* meaning that it doesn't matter what order you multiply the numbers: So you can pretend that the 2 and 4 are in the same fraction.

So, dividing the first numerator by 2 and the second denominator by 2, you get

$$\frac{2}{3} \times \frac{3}{4} = \frac{1}{3} \times \frac{3}{2}$$

But $\frac{1}{3} \times \frac{3}{2}$ has a 3 in the first denominator and a 3 in the second numerator. You can divide by 3!

So $\frac{1}{3} \times \frac{3}{2} = \frac{1}{1} \times \frac{1}{2} = \frac{1}{2}$, which is the same answer as in the original example.

In the previous example both methods — reducing before and after multiplying — were relatively easy. This example shows how necessary reducing before working the problem can be.

✔ Multiply the two fractions: $\frac{360}{121} \times \frac{77}{900}$

The numerator of the first fraction and the denominator of the second fraction can each be divided by 180.

$$\frac{360}{121} \times \frac{77}{900} = \frac{2}{121} \times \frac{77}{5}$$

The denominator of the first fraction and the numerator of the second fraction can each be divided by 11.

$$\frac{2}{121} \times \frac{77}{5} = \frac{2}{11} \times \frac{7}{5}$$

Now the multiplication is simple:

$$\frac{2}{11} \times \frac{7}{5} = \frac{14}{55}$$

This is much simpler than the original problem would have been!

The operations of addition and multiplication have another special feature that subtraction and division don't have. You can perform the operation on more than two fractions at a time.

✔ The following example shows how to multiply three fractions together. A situation such as this could happen if you were applying one discount after another to an original list price.

$$\frac{5}{6} \times \frac{3}{8} \times \frac{4}{7} = \frac{5 \times 3 \times 4}{6 \times 8 \times 7} = \frac{60}{336} = \frac{5}{28}$$

You can make this easier if you reduce first: the 4 and 8 in the third numerator and second denominator, and the 3 and 6 in the second numerator and first denominator.

✔ This example involves mixed numbers:

$$3\frac{1}{3} \times 5\frac{1}{4} \times 2 = \frac{10}{3} \times \frac{21}{4} \times \frac{2}{1}$$

Reducing first would mean dividing by 3 and dividing by 2.

$$\frac{10}{3} \times \frac{21}{4} \times \frac{2}{1} = \frac{10}{1} \times \frac{7}{2} \times \frac{1}{1} = \frac{70}{2} = 35$$

Dividing fractions

Dividing fractions is as easy as pie! It's just like multiplying fractions, except that the numerator and the denominator of the second fraction change places.

When dividing fractions:

1. **Change all mixed numbers to improper fractions.**

2. **Flip the second fraction, placing the bottom number on top and the top number on the bottom.**

3. **Continue as with the multiplication of fractions.**

The following example shows how this system works:

✔ You bought $6\frac{1}{2}$ pounds of sirloin steak and want to cut it into pieces that weigh $\frac{3}{4}$ of a pound each.

$$6\frac{1}{2} \div \frac{3}{4} = \frac{13}{2} \div \frac{3}{4} = \frac{13}{2} \times \frac{4}{3} = \frac{52}{6} = 8\frac{4}{6} = 8\frac{2}{3}$$

Having $8\frac{2}{3}$ pieces means that you can cut the steak into 8 pieces that each weigh a full $\frac{3}{4}$ pound with a small piece left over.

Dealing with Decimals

Decimals are nothing more than glorified fractions. They're special because their denominators are always 10, 100, 1,000, and so on — powers of ten. Because they're so special, you don't even have to bother with the denominator part. Just write the numerator and use a decimal point to indicate that it's really a fraction.

The decimal point symbol looks the same as a period at the end of a sentence, which is a really small figure, so you'll have to watch carefully for it. More importantly, though, you need to watch where the decimal point is placed in the number.

The number of decimal places to the right of the decimal point tells you the number of zeros in the power of ten that is written in the denominator.

Check out the decimal placement in the following examples:

- .3 has just one digit (3) to the right of the decimal point. The .3 is $\frac{3}{10}$.

- .408 has three digits (408) to the right of the decimal point. The .408 is $\frac{408}{1,000}$.

- 60.0003 has four digits (0003) to the right of the decimal point. The 60.0003 is 60 and $\frac{3}{10,000}$.

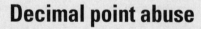

Decimal point abuse

When a decimal point is misused, it can be costly. Ninety-nine cents can use a cent symbol, 99¢, or a dollar symbol, $.99. It's when people aren't careful or don't understand that you see .99¢. You figure that they mean 99 cents, but that's not what this says. The price .99¢ means ninety-nine hundredths of a cent — not quite a cent.

A friend of mine once challenged a hamburger establishment on this. They advertised a super-duper hamburger for the regular price and any additional for .99¢. He went in and asked for his regular-priced hamburger and two additional for one cent each. (He was willing to round up to a whole penny.) When the flustered clerk finally realized what had happened, he honored my friend's request. Actually, the friend wouldn't have made a big deal of it. He just wanted to make a point. But you can bet that the sign was corrected quickly.

Decimal fractions are great because you can add, subtract, multiply, and divide them so easily. That's why it's often desirable to change a fraction to a decimal.

Changing fractions to decimals

All fractions can be changed to decimals. In Chapter 1, I tell you that rational numbers have decimals that can be written exactly as fractions. The decimal forms of rational numbers either end or repeat a pattern. Here is how you can change the fractions to decimals.

To change a fraction to a decimal, just divide the top by the bottom.

$$\frac{3}{4} \text{ becomes } 4\,\overline{)3.00} = .75 \text{ so } \frac{3}{4} = .75$$

$$\frac{15}{8} \text{ becomes } 8\,\overline{)15.000} = 1.875 \text{ so } \frac{15}{8} = 1.875$$

If the division doesn't come out evenly, you can stop after a certain number of decimal places and round off.

Rounding numbers:

1. **Determine the number of places you want and go one further.**

2. **Increase the last place you want by one number if the one further is five or bigger.**

3. **Leave the last place you want as is, if the one further is less than five.**

The fraction $\frac{5}{9}$ won't divide evenly, and it'll go on forever and ever when divided. So divide and decide when to stop.

Change $\frac{5}{9}$ to a decimal.

$$9\,\overline{)5.000000\ldots} = .5555\ldots$$

If you choose to round to three decimal places, $\frac{5}{9} = .55555\ldots \approx .556$.

The ≈ symbol means approximately the same or about equal. This is a useful symbol to use when rounding a number.

✔ Now try changing $1\frac{5}{8}$ to a decimal.

$$1\frac{5}{8} = \frac{13}{8}$$

$$8\overline{\smash{)}13.000} \atop 1.625$$

✔ Try changing $\frac{4}{7}$ to a decimal.

$$7\overline{\smash{)}4.000000000000\ldots} \atop .571428571428\ldots$$

If this is rounded to four places, the answer is $\frac{4}{7} \approx .5714$.

If this is rounded to five places, the answer is $\frac{4}{7} \approx .57143$.

Changing decimals to fractions

To change a decimal into a fraction, put the numbers to the right of the decimal point in a numerator. Put the number one in the denominator followed by as many zeros as the numerator has digits. Reduce the fraction if necessary.

✔ Change .36 into a fraction:

$$.36 = \frac{36}{100} = \frac{9}{25}$$

There were two digits in 36, so the 1 is followed by two zeros.

✔ Change .0005 into a fraction:

$$.0005 = \frac{5}{10,000} = \frac{1}{2,000}$$

Don't forget to count the zeros in front of the 5 when counting the number of digits.

✔ Change 3.025 into a fraction:

$$3.025 = 3\frac{25}{1,000} = 3\frac{1}{40}$$

You just need to be able to count decimal places and zeros.

Chapter 4

Exploring Exponents and Raising Radicals

*E*xponents, those small symbols, slightly higher and to the right of numbers, were developed so that mathematicians wouldn't have to keep repeating themselves! What is an exponent? An *exponent* is the small, superscripted number to the upper right of the larger number that tells you how many times you multiply the larger number, called the *base,* by itself. That is, three to the fourth power (3^4) is three multiplied by itself four times. Got that? Now, try it and see what happens.

$$3^4 = 3 \times 3 \times 3 \times 3 = [(3 \times 3) \times 3] \times 3 = 81$$

So, really, three to the fourth power (3^4) is another way of saying 81.

Multiplying the Same Thing Over and Over and . . .

When algebra was first written with symbols — instead of with all words — there were no exponents. If you wanted to multiply the variable y times itself six times, you'd write it:

yyyyyy. (Kinda like talking to a 3-year-old, "Why, why, why, why, why, why?") Writing the variable over and over can get tiresome (just like 3-year-olds), so the wonderful system of exponents was developed.

Powering up exponential notation

An *exponent* is a small number written above and to the right of the base — the number you're multiplying times itself. The exponent is usually in smaller print than the base. The base can be any real number. The exponent, the power, can be any real number, also. An exponent can be positive or negative or fractional or even a radical. What power! The following example gives you another demonstration of how convenient exponents can be:

$$x^n = x \cdot x \cdot x \cdot x \cdot x \ n \text{ times}$$

x: the base   *x* can be any real number.

n: the power, or exponent   *n* can be any real number.

Even though the *x* in the expression x^n can be any real number and the *n* can be any real number, they can't both be 0 at the same time. 0^0 really has no meaning in algebra. It takes a calculus course to discuss this. Also, if *x* is equal to 0, then *n* can't be negative.

In the examples that follow, the base is multiplied *n* times, and the exponential expression is evaluated.

$$2^4 = 2 \cdot 2 \cdot 2 \cdot 2 = 16$$
$$3^5 = 3 \cdot 3 \cdot 3 \cdot 3 \cdot 3 = 243$$
$$10^8 = 10 \cdot 10 \cdot 10 \cdot 10 \cdot 10 \cdot 10 \cdot 10 \cdot 10 = 100,000,000$$

The nice thing about exponents of ten is that the power tells you how many zeros are in the answer.

In this example, several bases are multiplied together. Each base has its own, separate exponent. The *x, y,* and *z* represent real numbers.

$$3^3 x^2 y^4 z^6 = 3 \cdot 3 \cdot 3 \cdot x \cdot x \cdot y \cdot y \cdot y \cdot y \cdot z \cdot z \cdot z \cdot z \cdot z \cdot z$$

You can see why it's preferable to use the powers. And in the next example, the base is actually a binomial. The parentheses mean that you add the two values together before applying the exponent.

$$(a + b)^3 = (a + b)(a + b)(a + b)$$

Comparing with exponents

It's easier to compare amounts when you use exponents. Try to compare two numbers: 943,260,000,000,000,000,000,000 and 8,720,000,000,000,000,000,000,000.

The first number may look bigger because of the first three digits, but this is deceiving.

If you write the numbers as exponential expressions you get

$$9.4326 \times 10^{23}$$

$$8.72 \times 10^{24}$$

The number with the higher power of ten is the larger number.

Why is the number with the higher power of ten larger? Look at these two numbers that are a little more manageable (they don't have over 20 zeros).

Compare 8×10^2 and 9×10^1. That's comparing $8 \times 100 = 800$ with $9 \times 10 = 90$. Even though the 9 is bigger than the 8, it's the larger power of ten that "wins."

Taking notes on scientific notation

Scientific notation is a standard way of recording very large and very small numbers so they can fit on one line on the page of a book and so they can be compared more easily. Computations with them are easier in this form, too.

The form for scientific notation is: $N \times 10^a$ where N is a number between 1 and 10 (but not 10 itself), and where a is an integer (positive or negative number).

Exponents

The first exponents appeared in about 1636 when the base was written on a regular line and the exponent was elevated a little to the right. The first exponents were expressed in Roman numerals, so *y* cubed would be written *y*^{III}. There were many who resisted using these, at first, and continued to write *y* cubed as *yyy*. Rene Descartes tended not to use two as an exponent. He still preferred to write *aa* rather than *a*^{2}. Isaac Newton is credited with being the first to recognize and use negative and fractional exponents.

You can write large and small numbers in scientific notation by moving the decimal point until the new form is a number from 1 to 10, and then indicating how many places the decimal point was moved by the power you raise 10 to.

Whether the power of ten is positive or negative depends on whether you move the decimal to the right or to the left. Moving the decimal to the right makes the exponent negative, moving it to the left gives you a positive exponent. The following examples show you how this works:

✔ $41,000 = 4.1 \times 10^4$

   Move the decimal place four spaces to the left, and, conveniently, you raise 10 to the fourth power.

✔ $312,000,000,000 = 3.12 \times 10^{11}$

   The decimal place is moved 11 spaces to the left.

✔ $.00000031 = 3.1 \times 10^{-7}$

   The decimal place is moved seven spaces to the right this time. This is a very small number, and the exponent is negative.

✔ $.2 = 2 \times 10^{-1}$

   The decimal place is moved one space to the right.

Exploring Exponential Expressions

Expressing very large numbers or very small numbers exponentially makes them so much easier to deal with! This is also true when studying situations that involve doing the same thing over and over again.

Picture a cat stalking a mouse. They're about 100 inches apart. Every time the mouse starts nibbling at the hunk of cheese, the cat takes advantage of the mouse's distraction and creeps closer by one-tenth the distance between them. The cat wants to get about six inches away — close enough to pounce. How far apart are they after four moves? How about after ten moves? How long will it take before the cat can pounce on the mouse? Use these steps to stalk your own mouse (or to figure any decreasing distance):

Find the distance remaining between the cat and mouse, which is nine-tenths. (One-tenth plus nine-tenths equals one — the whole amount.)

In each step, you multiply by $\frac{9}{10}$ — the fraction of the distance left after the move times the current distance. Nine-tenths times the current distance = new distance.

1. **Find the distance left between them after the first move by multiplying the current distance by $\frac{9}{10}$.**

   $\frac{9}{10}$ of $100 = \frac{9}{10} \times 100 = 90$ inches between them.

2. **Find the distance left between them after the second move by multiplying the current distance by $\frac{9}{10}$.**

   $\frac{9}{10}$ of $90 = \frac{9}{10} \times 90 = 81$ inches between them.

3. **Find the distance left between them after the third move by multiplying the current distance by $\frac{9}{10}$.**

   $\frac{9}{10}$ of $81 = \frac{9}{10} \times 81 = 72.9$ inches between them.

4. **Find the distance left between them after the fourth move by multiplying the current distance by $\frac{9}{10}$.**

   $\frac{9}{10}$ of $72.9 = \frac{9}{10} \times 72.9 = 65.61$ inches between them.

As you see, this can get pretty tedious. The best way to find the answer is to use exponents. Just follow these steps:

Distance to pounce $= 100\left(\frac{9}{10}\right)^n$ where n is the number of moves the cat has made.

In this formula, because the fraction $\frac{9}{10}$ is inside parentheses, apply the exponent just outside the parentheses to the fraction first. Multiply the fraction n times itself before multiplying it by 100.

✔ Find the distance between the cat and the mouse using this formula:

After the third move, the distance between them is $100\left(\frac{9}{10}\right)^3 = 72.9$ inches.

After the tenth move, the distance between them is $100\left(\frac{9}{10}\right)^{10} \approx 34.87$ inches. This still isn't close enough to pounce. I'm using the approximately symbol, $\approx$, here because the actual answer has many more decimal places and you don't need all that information.

After the twenty-sixth move, the distance between them is $100\left(\frac{9}{10}\right)^{26} \approx 6.46$ inches.

It'll take one more move to be within the six-inch pounce distance. Do you suppose the mouse still hadn't caught on after 26 moves? If not, then it deserves to be pounced upon.

Here's another quick example:

✔ To find the population of a city that is growing by 5 percent per year if it had 10,000 people in 1990, the equation needed is

$$\text{Population} = 10{,}000(1.05)^n$$

Let n be the number of years since 1990.

In 1995, $n = 5$, so the population is $10{,}000(1.05)^5 \approx 12{,}763$.

Round this to a whole number and use the approximately-equal-to sign so that there won't be a "piece" of a person.

Multiplying Exponents

You can multiply many exponential expressions together without having to change their form into the big or small numbers they represent. The only requirement is that the bases of the exponential expressions have to be the same. The answer is then a nice, neat exponential expression.

x^n: x is the base; it can be any real number. n is the power or exponent; it, too, can be any real number. To multiply two of these types of numbers together, the bases must be the same value. So, you can multiply $2^4 \cdot 2^6$ and $a^6 \cdot a^8$, but you cannot multiply $3^5 \cdot 4^5$ because the bases are not the same (although the exponents are).

To multiply powers of the same base, add the exponents together:

$$x^a \cdot x^b = x^{a+b}$$

Check out these examples:

- ✔ $2^4 \cdot 2^9 = 2^{4+9} = 2^{13}$
- ✔ $a^5 \cdot a^8 = a^{13}$
- ✔ $4^a \cdot 4^2 = 4^{a+2}$

If there's more than one base in an expression with powers, you can combine the numbers with the same bases, find the values, and then write them all together, as the following examples show:

- ✔ $3^2 \cdot 2^2 \cdot 3^3 \cdot 2^4 = 3^{2+3} \cdot 2^{2+4} = 3^5 \cdot 2^6$
- ✔ $4x^6y^5x^4y = 4x^{6+4}y^{5+1} = 4x^{10}y^6$

When there's no exponent showing, such as with y, you assume that the exponent is 1, so in this example write y^1.

Dividing and Conquering

As long as the bases are the same, you can divide exponential expressions, leaving the answers as exponential expressions.

To divide powers with the same base, subtract the exponents: $x^a \div x^b = x^{a-b}$ where x can be any real number except zero; you can't divide by zero.

These examples show how the division rule works:

  ✔ $2^{10} \div 2^4 = 2^{10-4} = 2^6$

  These exponentials represent the problem $1{,}024 \div 16 = 64$. It's much easier to leave these as exponents.

  ✔ $\dfrac{4x^6 y^3 z^2}{2x^4 y^3 z} = 2x^{6-4} y^{3-3} z^{2-1} = 2x^2 y^0 z^1 = 2x^2 z$:

  The variables represent numbers, so writing this out the long way would be

  $$\frac{2 \cdot 2 \cdot x \cdot x \cdot x \cdot x \cdot x \cdot x \cdot y \cdot y \cdot y \cdot z \cdot z}{2 \cdot x \cdot x \cdot x \cdot x \cdot y \cdot y \cdot y \cdot z}.$$

  By crossing out the common factors, all that's left is $2x^2 z$. Need I say more?

What's this with the exponent of 0 on the y? Read on.

Testing the Power of Zero

If x^3 means $x \cdot x \cdot x$, what does x^0 mean? Well, it doesn't mean x times zero, so the answer isn't zero. x represents some unknown real number; it just can't be zero. To understand how this works, use the following rule for division of exponential expressions involving zero.

Any number to the power of zero equals one, as long as the base number is not zero.

For example, to divide $2^4 \div 2^4$, use the rule for dividing exponential expressions, which says that if the base is the same, subtract the two exponents in the order that they're given. Doing this you find that the answer is 2^{4-4}. But $2^4 = 16$, so $2^4 \div 2^4 = 16 \div 16 = 1$. That means that $2^0 = 1$. This is true of all numbers that can be written as a division problem, which means that it's true for all numbers except those with a base of zero.

See how this power of zero works:

- ✔ $m^2 \div m^2 = m^{2-2} = m^0 = 1$
- ✔ $4x^3y^4z^7 \div 2x^3y^3z^7 = 2x^{3-3}y^{4-3}z^{7-7} = 2x^0y^1z^0 = 2y$
- ✔ $\dfrac{(2x^2 + 3x)^4}{(2x^2 + 3x)^4} = (2x^2 + 3x)^{4-4} = (2x^2 + 3x)^0 = 1$

Notice that the x and z, with their zero exponents, then become ones. And when you multiply by one, the value is unchanged.

Working with Negative Exponents

Negative exponents are a neat little creation. They mean something very specific and have to be handled with care, but they are oh, so convenient to have.

You can use a negative exponent to write a fraction without writing a fraction! It's a way to combine expressions with the same base, whether the different factors are in the numerator or denominator or whatever. It's a way to change division problems into multiplication problems.

Negative exponents are a way of writing powers of fractions or decimals without using the fraction or decimal. For instance, instead of writing $\left(\dfrac{1}{10}\right)^{14}$ you can write 10^{-14}.

A reciprocal of a number is the multiplicative inverse of the number. The product of a number and its reciprocal is equal to one.

The reciprocal of x^a is $\dfrac{1}{x^a}$, which can be written as x^{-a}. The variable x is any real number except zero, and a is any real number. And, going to the negative side, $x^{-a} = \dfrac{1}{x^a}$.

The following examples show you how to change from positive to negative exponents, and vice versa:

✔ $2^{-3} = \frac{1}{2^3} = \frac{1}{8}$

The reciprocal of 2^3 is $\frac{1}{2^3} = 2^{-3}$.

✔ $z^{-4} = \frac{1}{z^4}$

The reciprocal of z^4 is $\frac{1}{z^4} = z^{-4}$. In this case, z cannot be 0.

✔ $6^{-1} = \frac{1}{6}$

The reciprocal of 6 is $\frac{1}{6} = 6^{-1}$.

But what if you start out with a negative exponent in the denominator? What happens then? The reciprocal of $\frac{1}{3^{-4}}$ is 3^4. Here you start with a negative exponent because $\frac{1}{3^4} = 3^{-4}$. The reciprocal is $\frac{1}{3^{-4}} = 3^4$.

So the negative exponent in the denominator comes up to the numerator with a change in the sign to a positive exponent. Here are two more examples:

✔ $\dfrac{x^2 y^3}{3z^{-4}} = \dfrac{x^2 y^3 z^4}{3}$

✔ $\dfrac{4a^3 b^5 c^6 d}{a^{-1} b^{-2}} = 4a^3 a^1 b^5 b^2 c^6 d = 4a^4 b^7 c^6 d$

Powers of Powers

Because exponents are symbols for repeated multiplication, one way to write $(x^3)^6$ is $x^3 \cdot x^3 \cdot x^3 \cdot x^3 \cdot x^3 \cdot x^3$. Using the multiplication rule where you just add all the exponents together, you get $x^{3+3+3+3+3+3} = x^{18}$. Wouldn't it be just grand if the rule for raising a power to a power was just to multiply the two exponents together? Lucky you!

Raising a power to a power: $(x^n)^m = x^{n \cdot m}$. When the whole expression, x^n, is raised to the mth power, the new power of x is determined by multiplying n and m together.

These examples show you how raising a power to a power works:

✔ $\left(6^{-3}\right)^{4} = 6^{-3\cdot4} = 6^{-12} = \dfrac{1}{6^{12}}$

✔ $\left(3^{2}\right)^{-5} = 3^{2(-5)} = 3^{-10} = \dfrac{1}{3^{10}}$

✔ $(3x^{-2}y)^{2} = 3^{2}x^{2} \cdot 2y^{3\cdot2} = 9x^{4}y^{6}$

✔ $(3x^{2}y^{3})^{2} = 3^{2}x^{2\cdot2}y^{3\cdot2} = 9x^{4}y^{6}$

(Each factor in the parentheses is raised to the power outside the parentheses.)

✔ $\left(3x^{-2}y\right)^{2}\left(2xy^{-3}\right)^{4} = \left(3^{2}x^{-2\cdot2}y^{1\cdot2}\right)\left(2^{4}x^{1\cdot4}y^{-3\cdot4}\right) =$
$\left(9x^{-4}y^{2}\right)\left(16x^{4}y^{-12}\right) = 144x^{0}y^{-10} = \dfrac{144}{y^{10}}$

Notice that the order of operations is observed here. First you raise the expressions in the parentheses to their powers. Then multiply the two expressions together. You get to see multiplying exponents (raising a power to a power) and adding exponents (multiplying same bases). Next is an example with negative exponents.

$$(x^{2}y^{3})^{-2}(x^{2}y^{-3})^{-4} = (x^{2(-2)}y^{3(-2)})(x^{(-2)(-4)}y^{(-3)(-4)})$$
$$=(x^{-4}y^{-6})(x^{8}y^{12}) = x^{-4+8}y^{-6+12} = x^{4}y^{6}$$

Squaring Up to Square Roots

When you do square roots, the symbol for that operation is a radical, $\sqrt{\ }$.

The radical is a nonbinary operation (involving just one number) that asks you, "What number times itself gives you this number under the radical?" Another way of saying this is if $\sqrt{a} = b$, then $b^{2} = a$.

Finding square roots is a relatively common operation in algebra, but working with and combining the roots isn't always so clear.

Expressions with radicals can be multiplied or divided as long as the root power or value under the radical is the same. Expressions with radicals *cannot* be added or subtracted unless *both* the root power and the value under the radical are the same.

Here are some examples showing what I mean:

✔ $\sqrt{2} + \sqrt{3}$

These cannot be combined because it's addition, and the value under the radical is not the same.

✔ $\sqrt{2} \cdot \sqrt{3} = \sqrt{6}$

These can be combined because it's multiplication, and the root power is the same.

✔ $\sqrt{8} \div \sqrt{4} = \sqrt{2}$

These can be combined because it's division, and the root power is the same.

✔ $\sqrt{3} - \sqrt[4]{3}$

These cannot be combined because it's subtraction, and the root power isn't the same.

When the numbers inside the radical are the same, you can see some nice combinations involving addition and subtraction. Multiplication and division can be performed whether they're the same or not. The root power refers to square root, $\sqrt{}$, cube root, $\sqrt[3]{}$, fourth root, $\sqrt[4]{}$, and so on.

The rules for adding, subtracting, multiplying, and dividing radical expressions are best summarized below.

Radical rules: Assume that a and b are positive values.

✔ $m\sqrt{a} + n\sqrt{a} = (m + n)\sqrt{a}$

Addition and subtraction can be performed if the root power and value under the radical are the same.

✔ $m\sqrt{a} - n\sqrt{a} = (m - n)\sqrt{a}$

✔ $\sqrt{a} \cdot \sqrt{a} = \sqrt{a^2} = a$

✔ $\sqrt{a} \cdot \sqrt{b} = \sqrt{ab}$

Multiplication and division can be performed if the root powers are the same.

✔ $\dfrac{\sqrt{a}}{\sqrt{b}} = \sqrt{\dfrac{a}{b}}$

The convention that mathematicians have adopted is to use fractions in the powers to indicate that this stands for a root or a radical.

> ✔ $\sqrt{x} = x^{1/2}$
>
> ✔ $\sqrt[3]{x} = x^{1/3}$
>
> ✔ $\sqrt[4]{x} = x^{1/4}$
>
> ✔ $\sqrt{4ab} = (4ab)^{1/2} = (4)^{1/2}a^{1/2}b^{1/2} = 2a^{1/2}b^{1/2}$
>
> ✔ $\sqrt[3]{x^2y} = \left(x^2\right)^{1/3}y^{1/3} = x^{2/3}y^{1/3}$

When there's no number outside and to the upper left of the radical, you assume that it's a two.

Recall that when raising a power to a power, you multiply the exponents. This is discussed in the "Powers of Powers" section, earlier in the chapter.

When changing from radical form to fractional exponents:

> ✔ $\sqrt[n]{a} = a^{1/n}$
>
> The nth root of a can be written as a fractional exponent with a raised to the reciprocal of that power.
>
> ✔ $\sqrt[n]{a^m} = a^{m/n}$
>
> When the nth root of a^m is taken, it's raised to the $\frac{1}{n}$ power. Using the "Powers of Powers" rule, the m and the $\frac{1}{n}$ are multiplied together.

This rule allows you to simplify the following expressions. Note that when using the "Powers of Powers" rule, the bases still have to be the same.

> ✔ $6x^2 \cdot \sqrt[3]{x} = 6x^2 \cdot x^{1/3} = 6x^{2+1/3} = 6x^{7/3}$
>
> ✔ $3\sqrt{x} \cdot \sqrt[4]{x^3} \cdot x = 3x^{1/2} \cdot x^{3/4} \cdot x^1 = 3x^{9/4}$
>
> Leave the exponent as $\frac{9}{4}$. Don't write it as a mixed number.
>
> ✔ $4\sqrt{x} \cdot \sqrt[3]{a} = 4x^{1/2}a^{1/3}$
>
> These can't really be combined because the bases are not the same.

Chapter 5

Doing Operations in Order and Checking Your Answers

. . . .

In This Chapter

▶ Organizing your operations into bite-size pieces

▶ Ordering your problem solving from first to last

▶ Making sure your answers make sense

▶ Writing your answers correctly

. . . .

*I*n agebra, the order of operations is a biggie that you use frequently. It tells you what to do first, next, and last in a problem, whether terms are in grouping symbols or raised to a power.

And, because you may not always remember the order of operations correctly, it's very important to check your work. Making sure that the answer you get makes sense, and that it actually solves the problem is the final step of working every problem. The very final step is writing the solution in a way that other folks can understand easily.

Ordering Operations

Mathematicians designed rules so that anyone reading a mathematical expression could do it the same way and get the same answer. In the case of multiple signs and operations, working out the problems needs to be done in a specified order, from the first to the last. This is the order of operations.

Order of operations: Work out the operations and signs in the following order:

1. **Powers or roots**

2. **Multiplication or division**

3. **Addition or subtraction**

When you have two operations on the same "level," you can do those in any order. So, if there's both a power and a root, either can be done first. If you have more than two operations, do them in order from left to right, following the order of operations.

If the problem contains grouped items, do what's inside a grouping symbol first, then follow the order of operations. The grouping symbols are

✔ **Parentheses ():** Parentheses are the most commonly used symbols for grouping.

✔ **Brackets [ ] and Braces { }:** Brackets and braces are also used frequently for grouping and have the same effect as parentheses. Using the different types of symbols helps when there's more than one grouping in a problem. It's easier to tell where a group starts and ends.

Calculating differences in brackets

In algebra problems, parentheses, brackets, and braces are all used for grouping. Terms inside the grouping symbols have to be operated upon before they can be acted upon by anything outside the grouping symbol. All the bracket types have equal weight; none is more powerful or acts differently from the others. This does not carry through with many graphing calculators. The brackets and braces mean something entirely different in those instruments. In most graphing calculators

✔ Brackets mean that the items inside are a part of a matrix, a rectangular arrangement of numbers.

✔ Braces mean that what's inside is part of a list of numbers.

These differences make for some awkward situations when you want to show several groupings within a single expression. Because you're limited to parentheses only, and they're all the same size, there's often confusion as to where a grouping starts and where it ends.

> ✔ **Radical** $\sqrt{}$: This is used for finding roots.
>
> ✔ **Fraction Line (Vinculum)** —: The fraction line also acts as a grouping symbol — everything above the line in the numerator is grouped together, and everything below the line in the denominator is grouped together.

Even though the order of operations and grouping symbol rules are fairly straightforward, it's hard to describe, in words, all the situations that can come up in these problems. The examples in this chapter should clear up any questions you may have.

The following problem doesn't have parentheses or brackets to indicate what operation needs to be done first, but according to the order of operations, you multiply and divide before adding and subtracting. To find the solution to $8 - 3 \times 4 + 6 \div 2$, for example, follow these steps:

1. **Multiply 3×4 and divide $6 \div 2$ to get 12 and 3.**

   The parentheses help emphasize what to do first.

   $$8 - (3 \times 4) + (6 \div 2) = 8 - 12 + 3$$

2. **Add and subtract in order from left to right.**

   $$8 - 12 + 3 = -1$$
   $$8 - 3 \times 4 + 6 \div 2 = -1$$

In this example, the operations are grouped to help you.

$$[8 \div (5 - 3)] \times 5 =$$

1. **Subtract $5 - 3$ in the parentheses to get 2.**

2. **Divide 8 by 2 and multiply that answer by 5.**

   $$[8 \div 2] \times 5$$

3. **Multiply 4 times 5.**

   $$[8 \div 2] \times 5 = 4 \times 5 = 20$$

Don't let the division in the next problem put you off. It's easy!

To solve $\dfrac{4(7+5)}{2+1}$:

1. **Add the 7 and 5 in the numerator, then the 2 and 1 in the denominator.**

$$\frac{4\,(12)}{3}$$

Remember that the fraction line is a grouping symbol. The 2 and 1 in the denominator are grouped together and have to be added first, before you divide the sum into the numerator.

2. Multiply and divide to get

$$\frac{4\,(12)}{3} = \frac{48}{3} = 16$$

Although any operations in parentheses or brackets take precedence, exponents and roots should be solved first, according to the order of operations. Now you can work out a problem with exponents.

$$2 + 3^2\,(5 - 1) =$$

1. Subtract the 1 from the 5 in the parenthesis to get 4.

$$2 + 3^2(4)$$

2. Raise the 3 to the second power to get 9.

$$2 + 9(4)$$

3. Multiply the 9 and 4 to get 36.

$$2 + 9(4) = 2 + 36$$

4. Calculate the final answer.

$$2 + 36 = 38$$

Engineering the great pyramids

The Egyptians were strong in geometry and developed rough formulas to find the volume of various solid figures. They put this knowledge to work building the pyramids, which are not only engineering marvels but mathematical marvels as well. With relatively primitive tools, such as levers and plumb lines, the Egyptians cut stones that varied, on average, by about $\frac{1}{100}$ of an inch, and they were brought together to within $\frac{1}{500}$ inch. The Great Pyramid of Cheops has sides that face directly north, south, east, and west, correct to $\frac{1}{12}$ of a degree.

Try this problem involving a square root on for size. Remember to work any operation in parentheses or brackets first.

$$(3+4)\sqrt{25} - 8$$

1. **Add 3 + 4.**

$$7\sqrt{25} - 8$$

2. **Find the square root of 25.**

$$7 \times 5 - 8$$

3. **Multiply the 7 and 5.**

$$35 - 8$$

4. **Solve the problem.**

Since $35 - 8 = 27$, then $(3+4)\sqrt{25} - 8 = 27$.

Be sure to catch the subtle difference between the two expressions here: -2^4 and $(-2)^4$. The expression $-2^4 = -16$ because the order of operations says to first raise to the fourth power and then apply the minus sign.

The expression $(-2)^4 = 16$ because the entire result in the parentheses is raised to the fourth power. This is equivalent to multiplying -2 by itself four times. That's an even number of negative signs, so the result is positive.

In general, if you want a negative number raised to a power, you have to put it in parentheses with the power outside.

Checking Your Answers

Checking your answers when doing algebra is always a good idea, just like reconciling your checkbook with your bank statement is a good idea. Actually, checking answers in algebra is easier and more fun than reconciling a checking account. Or, maybe your checking account is more fun than mine.

Check your answers in algebra on two levels.

> ✓ **Level 1: Does the answer make any sense?**
>
> If your checkbook balance shows $40 million, does that make any sense? Sure, we'd all like it to be that, but for

most of us this would be a red flag that something is wrong with our computations.

✔ **Level 2: Does actually putting the answer back into the problem give you a true statement? Does it work?**

This is the more critical check because it gives you more exact information about your answer. The first level helps weed out the obvious errors. This is the final check.

The next sections help you make even more sense of these checks.

Making sense at level 1

To check as to whether an answer makes any sense or not, you have to know something about the topic. These situations should involve things you're familiar with. Just use your common sense.

For instance, your answer to an algebra problem is $x = 5$. If you're solving for Jon's weight in pounds, unless Jon is a guinea pig instead of a person, you probably want to go back and redo the work. Five pounds doesn't make any sense as an answer in this context.

On the other hand, if the problem involves a number of pennies in a person's pocket, then five pennies seems reasonable. Getting five as the number of home runs a player hit in one ballgame may at first seem quite possible, but if you think about it, five home runs in one game is a lot — even for Sammy Sosa or Mark McGuire. You may want to double-check.

Plugging in level 2

Actually plugging in your answer requires you to go through the algebra manipulations in the problem. You add, subtract, multiply, and divide to see if you get a true statement using your answer.

For example, suppose Jack has four more pennies than Jill. If they have a total of 14 pennies altogether, then how many pennies does Jill have? Suppose you worked the problem and came up with $x = 5$. Now check:

1. **Write the problem.**

   Let x represent the number of pennies that Jill has. Jack has $x + 4$ pennies. That means $x + (x + 4) = 14$.

   The number of pennies Jill has plus the number of pennies Jack has equals 14.

2. **Insert the answer into the equation.**

   Replace the variable with 5 to get $5 + (5 + 4) = 14$.

3. **Do the operations and check to see if the answer works.**

   $5 + 9 = 14$ is a true statement, so the problem checks. Jill has 5 pennies; Jack has 4 more than that, or 9 pennies; altogether, they have 14 pennies.

In the next example, you solved for x in the following equation and came up with the answer 2.

$$5x[x + 3(x^2 - 3)] + 1 = 0$$

To check, replace the variable with 2 to get $5 \cdot 2[2 + 3(2^2 - 3)] + 1 = 0$.

Do the operations and simplify:

Square the 2 to get $5 \cdot 2\ [2 + 3(4 - 3)] + 1 = 0$.

Subtract in the parentheses to get $5 \cdot 2[2 + 3(1)] + 1 = 0$.

Add in the bracket to get $5 \cdot 2[5] + 1 = 0$.

Multiply the 5, 2, and 5 to get $50 + 1 \neq 0$.

This time the work does not check. You should go back and try again to find a value for x that works.

Writing Understandable Answers

An algebraic expression may be written in all sorts of ways, which may all be correct, but the different ways of writing may not necessarily be nice, pretty, or useful. Yes, algebra can be pretty, and in this section I show you how.

In any one term, put the numbers first, and then let the variables follow in alphabetical order. Put radicals at the end.

To put *ed*3*ac* in standard format, write the number first, then alphabetize the variables: 3*acde*.

When arranging a string of terms, take all the terms containing the same variable and put them in either increasing or decreasing powers of that variable. For example, to put terms in decreasing powers of a variable, find the term that contains the highest power of that variable, put it first, and then find the next highest, put it second, and so on. The choice of variable and whether it's increasing or decreasing depends on the situation and what you're going to do next. If a problem involves solving for the value of the variable x, and the problem has several powers of x, write the terms in order of the powers of x — whether the order is decreasing or increasing.

To illustrate this, check out the following examples. Each individual term is written correctly, but the terms need to be put in some order.

- ✔ Option 1 is in *increasing* powers of x. Note that the lowest power of x comes first.

$$3xy^2 + 8x^2y^3 - 4x^3y$$

- ✔ The second option is in decreasing powers of x. This time the highest power of x comes first.

$$-4x^3y + 8x^2y^3 + 3xy^2$$

- ✔ You can switch variables, and write in terms of the increasing powers of y.

$$-4x^3y + 3xy^2 + 8x^2y^3$$

- ✔ Stick with y, but write the terms in decreasing powers of y.

$$8x^2y^3 + 3xy^2 - 4x^3y$$

Using these conventions makes your notation more understandable to the people who read your work.

Chapter 6

Prepping for Operations

· ·

In This Chapter

▶ Expressing yourself algebraically

▶ Operating on assumptions

▶ Adding and subtracting under consideration

▶ Multiplying and dividing coefficients and variables

· ·

*W*ork in algebra is done using variables (letters) and symbols (see more on variables and symbols in Chapter 1). These are like shorthand notation — quicker and easier to write than all the big words in longhand. But, with shorthand, you have to know what everything means and how it goes together. In algebra, simple arithmetic rules are transformed into rules for adding, subtracting, multiplying, and dividing variables. Letting variables represent numbers allows for more flexibility, but you have to be careful — everything is disguised.

Realizing Some Restrictions

When algebra uses variables to represent numbers that can be added, subtracted, multiplied, and divided, you assume that the variables are representing quantities or amounts that can be added, subtracted, multiplied, and divided. But using the representation is not quite that simple or obvious. Even when you're just adding numbers together, restrictions exist. Likewise, there are restrictions and rules when you're adding variables together or numbers and variables together.

When adding quantities or amounts, you have to be sure that the amounts can be added. For example, if you want to add quarters and dimes, then count the number of coins and say that you have ten coins, or change to the money value of each coin and say that you have $1.90. Adding like to like is even more critical when you add letters because silly errors aren't as obvious.

Representing Numbers with Letters

"This segment is sponsored by the letter b, standing in for a number to be determined later." Okay, so that's a bad take-off on *Sesame Street,* but I hope you see what I'm driving at. In algebra, letters stand in for numbers all the time.

Letting a variable represent a quantity can simplify a problem and lead to nice, neat situations because you don't have to deal with a bunch of messy words. Sometimes you do have to deal with some fairly complicated situations. But fear not! A few simple rules can help change even the most complicated situation into an easily understandable one.

Attaching factors and coefficients

One nice thing about algebra is that it conserves energy — the energy that would be needed to write multiplication symbols between letters. Even having to write dots between symbols takes time, so a simpler system was devised. When a number is written in front of a variable, such as $3x$, it means that the 3 and x are multiplied together. The 3 is a coefficient in this case.

A number preceding a variable is a *coefficient.* For example, the number 4 is the coefficient when $a + a + a + a$ is expressed as $4a$.

When several variables are multiplied together, multiplication symbols aren't needed. The term $3xyz$ means that all four factors are multiplied together.

Provided that the number is directly in front of the variable, $2a$ means that 2 and a are multiplied together. So $2a$ is two times, or twice, a. Twice as many apples means that if a represents 10 apples, then $2a$ represents 2 times 10, or 20 apples.

The symbols + and – may mean many things to you. They mean many things in algebra, too. It all depends on the context. These symbols always separate terms, which are clusters of variables and numbers connected by multiplication and division. Plus and minus signs separate terms from one another.

In algebra-speak, a plus sign means *and, more, increased by, added to,* and so on. The expression 2 + *a* could represent

- A gift of *a* dollars has increased my pocket change up from two dollars.
- Two people went through the door, and then *a* more went in.
- The temperature was two degrees, and then it went up *a* degrees.

This is all different from the term 2*a* in which the coefficient 2 doubles the amount of the variable *a*.

The minus sign means *less, take away, decreased by, subtracted from,* and so on. The expression *a* – 2 could represent:

- There were *a* administrators, but their number was decreased by two.
- There were two less than *a* alligators in the pond.
- William Tell had *a* apples when he started and two fewer when he finished.

Doing the Math

Addition was probably the first operation you discovered. It's the easiest for people of all ages to picture and relate to. Adding is a bit trickier in algebra just because so often you can't add. But when you can, it's a nice process.

Adding and subtracting variables

When adding, instead of expressing the long way, you can just write 4*a*, which says the same thing more efficiently because multiplication is just repeated addition. In the case of 4*a*, the number represented by a is added four times. Or, you can say that a is multiplied by four.

By expressing $a + a + a + a$ as $4a$, however, you are creating a single term, which is math jargon for coefficient(s) and/or variable(s) grouped together but sometimes separated from other terms by a plus or minus sign. So, the following operation, where the variables a, b, and c represent any real numbers, has three terms:

$$10ab + 3c - 7c$$

When adding or subtracting terms that have exactly the same variables, combine the coefficients.

When adding $2a + 5a + 4a$, what is the result?

Because you have three separate quantities, and each of them has an a, you can add them together.

A variable that appears more than once in an expression or equation always represents the same number. If the variable could represent more than one thing, the statement would be worthless — with no way to tell one meaning of the variable from another.

Now try adding up the same variable in the following example:

$$2a = a + a$$

$$5a = a + a + a + a + a$$

$$4a = a + a + a + a$$

That's a total of 11 a variables altogether. Notice that the numbers in front, the coefficients 2, 5, and 4, add up to 11, also.

$$2a + 5a + 4a = (2 + 5 + 4)a = 11a$$

When adding or subtracting terms with the same variable (such as x or n in the following examples), add or subtract the coefficients (numbers in front of the variables), and let the result stand alongside the variable. If a, b, and c are coefficients of the variable x, then

$$ax + bx - cx = (a + b - c)x$$

When there is no number in front of the variable, assume that the number is one. (This is one of the few times you can assume something and not make a donkey of yourself.)

$$a = 1a$$

$$x = 1x$$

The following example shows you how one variable can be added to another term with the same variable:

$$a + 3a + x + 2x = 1a + 3a + 1x + 2x = 4a + 3x$$

Notice that you add terms that have the same variables because they represent the same amounts. You don't try to add the terms with different variables. The examples that follow involve two or more variables:

$$5a + 2a + 6b + 8b + 11c = 7a + 14b + 11c$$

$$3x + 4y - 2x - 8y + x = 2x - 4y$$

When subtracting terms, use the rules for adding and subtracting signed numbers and apply them to the coefficients. (Check out Chapter 2 for information on working with signed numbers.)

$$5a + 4a - 2a + 6 + 3b - 2b = 7a + b + 6$$

Notice that the 6 doesn't have a variable. It stands by itself; it isn't multiplying anything.

Adding and subtracting with powers

The following examples show how addition and subtraction are performed on several terms involving variables. Notice that the terms that combine always have exactly the same variables with exactly the same powers. For more on powers (exponents), see Chapter 4.

- ✔ $x + x + x = 3x$
- ✔ $x^2 - 2x^2 + 3x^2 + 3x^2 = 5x^2$

✔ $x + 3x + 4x^2 + 5x^2 + 6x^3 = 4x + 9x^2 + 6x^3$

✔ $4x^4 - 3x^3 + 2x^2 + x - 1$

In the last example, none of the powers (exponents) are the same, so even though the variables are the same, you can't add the numbers in front together.

In order to add or subtract terms with the same variable, the exponents of the variable must be the same. Perform the required operations on the coefficients, leaving the variable and exponent as they are.

Multiplying and Dividing Variables

Multiplying variables is in some ways easier than adding or subtracting them, but you still have to be a bit careful. When you divide variables, however, you need to follow some relatively strict rules. In the following sections, I give you the tips and rules.

Multiplying variables

When the variables are the same, multiplying them together "compresses" them into a single factor (variable). But you still can't combine different variables.

When multiplying variables, multiply the coefficients and variables as usual. If the bases are the same, you can multiply the bases by merely adding their exponents. (See more on the multiplication of exponents in Chapter 4.) Write the result in a compact form.

Look at these examples where the letters are the variables as well as the bases:

✔ $a \cdot a \cdot b \cdot c = a^2bc$

✔ $2 \cdot a \cdot a \cdot a \cdot b \cdot b \cdot c = 2a^3b^2c$

✔ $2 \cdot a \cdot a \cdot a \cdot a \cdot 3 \cdot b \cdot b \cdot b \cdot 4 \cdot c \cdot c = 24a^4b^3c^2$

✔ $2 \cdot a^2 \cdot a^3 \cdot 3 \cdot b \cdot b \cdot b^6 \cdot 5 \cdot c \cdot c^2 \cdot c^{10} = 30a^5b^8c^{13}$

✔ $(2a^2b^2c^3)(4a^3b^2c^4) = 8a^{2+3}\,b^{2+2}\,c^{3+4} = 8a^5b^4c^7$

✔ $(3x^2yz^{-2})(4x^2y^2z^4)(3xyz) = 36x^{2-2+1}y^{1+2+1}z^{-2+4+1} = 36xy^4z^3$

Dividing variables

When you want to divide a combination of variables and numbers, divide the numbers as if you're reducing fractions (see Chapter 3 for fraction reduction). But only variables that are alike can be divided.

When dividing variables, write the problem as a fraction. Using the greatest common factor, divide the numbers and reduce. Use the rules of exponents (see Chapter 4) to divide variables that are the same.

Dividing variables is fairly straightforward. Each variable is considered separately. The number coefficients are reduced the same as in simple fractions.

This can be explained with aluminum cans: Four friends decided to collect aluminum cans for recycling (and money). They collected $12x^3$ cans, and they're going to get y^2 cents per can. The total amount of money collected is then $12x^3y^2$ cents. How will they divvy this up?

Divide the total amount by four to get the individual amount that each of the four friends will receive. $\dfrac{12x^3y^2}{4} = 3x^3y^2$ cents each. The only thing that divides here is the coefficient.

If you want the number of cans each will get paid for, divide $\dfrac{12x^3y^2}{4y^2} = 3x^3$ cans.

Why is using variables better than using just numbers? Because if the numbers change, then you still have all the shares worked out. Just let the x and y change in value. Work through the following examples to find out how to divide using variables, coefficients, and exponents:

✔ If a stands for the number of apples, ten apples divided into groups of five apples each results in two groups (not two apples).

$$\frac{10a}{5a} = 2$$

Ten apples divided into five groups results in two apples per group.

➤ $\frac{6a^2}{3a} = 2a$

Three divides six twice. Using the rules of exponents, $a^2 \div a = a$.

I prefer to write the answer with x in the denominator and a positive exponent rather than in the numerator with a negative exponent.

$$\frac{14x^2}{7x^4} = 2x^{-2} = \frac{2}{x^2}$$

Doing It All

The four main operations, addition, subtraction, multiplication, and division, are covered in the preceding sections. Many algebra problems involve more than one operation, so look at the following steps to see how to handle a combination of operations.

In this example, the operations are performed on

$$4a^2b^3(2a^3b^2) + 5ab^{-2}(2a^4b^7) + 5$$

1. **Multiply the variables together separately in each term.**

   $$4 \cdot 2a^2a^3b^3b^2 + 5 \cdot 2aa^4b^{-2}b^7 + 5$$

2. **Add the exponents of the variables that are alike.**

   $$8a^{2+3}b^{3+2} + 10a^{1+4}b^{-2+7} + 5$$

   $$8a^5b^5 + 10a^5b^5 + 5$$

   You can see that the first two terms are alike as far as the variables they have and the exponents on those variables, which is why you can add them together.

3. **Combine terms that are alike.**

   $$(8 + 10)a^5b^5 + 5 = 18a^5b^5 + 5$$

Okay. Now that you have successfully met the challenge of performing several operations on one complex example, why not try going through the steps again to perform a combination of operations on another example?

$$3m^2(2mn) - 4m^3n^3(2n^{-2}) + 5m^2n^3 - 6mn(mn)$$

1. **Multiply the variables together separately in each term.**

$$3 \cdot 2m^2mn - 4 \cdot 2m^3n^3n^{-2} + 5m^2n^3 - 6mmnn$$

2. **Add the exponents of the variables that are alike.**

$$6m^{2+1}n - 8m^3n^{3-2} + 5m^2n^3 - 6m^{1+1}\,n^{1+1}$$

$$6m^3n - 8m^3n + 5m^2n^3 - 6m^2n^2$$

3. **Combine the terms that are alike.**

In this case, only the first two terms can be combined; their variables and their exponents match.

$$(6 - 8)m^3n + 5m^2n^3 - 6m^2n^2 = -2m^3n + 5m^2n^3 - 6m^2n^2$$

The following example is your chance to strut your stuff. You've done the multiplying, so the next step is division (which is really simple subtraction). Go for it!

In this example, the operations are performed on

$$\frac{4x^2y^3}{2xy} - \frac{15xy^5}{3y^3} + \frac{13x^{-2}y^{11}}{x^{-5}y^8} + \frac{11x^4y^{7/2}}{xy^{1/2}}$$

1. **Divide by subtracting the exponents of the common bases.**

Divide the known numbers. Assume that the base without an exponent has one for an exponent. This problem has negative exponents to deal with in both the numerator and the denominator.

$$2x^{2-1}y^{3-1} - 5xy^{5-3} + 13x^{-2+5}y^{11-8} + 11x^{4-1}y^{7/2-1/2}$$

2. **Complete the subtraction on the exponents.**

Note: When the negative exponent (–5) that was in the denominator was brought up, it became positive and was added. Fractional exponents work just like other whole number exponents; they add and subtract just the same.

$$2xy^2 - 5xy^2 + 13x^3y^3 + 11x^3y^3$$

3. **Add or subtract the terms that are exactly alike — numbers that have variables and exponents in common.**

$$(2-5)xy^2 + (13+11)x^3y^3 = -3xy^2 + 24x^3y^3$$

In this last example, the rule for multiplying exponents is used in two of the terms. For more on this, see Chapter 4.

Perform the operations on $(3x^2y)^2 + 5x^4y - (2xy^{1/2})^4 - 16xy^4$

1. **Raise powers to powers by multiplying the exponents.**

$$3^{1\cdot2}x^{2\cdot2}y^{1\cdot2} + 5x^4y - 2^{1\cdot4}x^{1\cdot4}y^{(1/2)\cdot4} - 16xy^4$$

2. **Multiply the values in the exponents.**

$$3^2x^4y^2 + 5x^4y - 16x^4y^2 - 16xy^4$$

$$9x^4y^2 + 5x^4y - 16x^4y^2 - 16xy^4$$

3. **Combine any terms that have variables that are alike.**

$$(9-16)x^4y^2 + 5x^4y - 16xy^4 = -7x^4y^2 + 5x^4y - 16xy^4$$

You deal with terms that have exponents outside the parentheses first. Then you can combine the terms that have the exact same powers on x and y.

Chapter 7

Working with Numbers in Their Prime

● ●

In This Chapter

▶ Perplexing and mysterious prime numbers

▶ Bringing big numbers down to size: Divisibility rules!

▶ Investigating composite numbers: Prime factorization

▶ Finding factoring methods

● ●

*P*rime numbers are important in algebra because they help you work with the smallest possible numbers. Big numbers are often unwieldy and can produce more computation errors. So reducing fractions to their lowest terms and factoring expressions to make problems more manageable are basic tasks.

Beginning with the Basics

A *prime number* is a whole number larger than the number one that can be divided evenly only by itself and one.

The first and smallest prime number is the number two. It's the only *even* prime number. All primes after two are odd because all even numbers can be divided evenly by one, themselves, and two. They don't fit the definition of a prime number.

If a number divides evenly by 3, adding up the digits in the number gives you a multiple of 3.

Table 7-1 lists the first 25 prime numbers. Confirm for yourself that each can be divided evenly *only* by itself and one.

Why isn't the number 1 prime?

By tradition and definition, the number 1 is not prime. The definition of a prime number is that it can be divided evenly only by itself and 1. In this case, there would be a double hit, because 1 is itself.

Many theorems and conjectures involving primes don't work if 1 is included. Mathematicians around the time of Pythagoras sometimes even excluded the number 2 from the list of primes because they didn't consider 1 or 2 to be true numbers — they were just generators of all other even and odd numbers. Sometimes it seems that some rules are a bit arbitrary. In this case, it just makes everything else work better if 1 isn't a prime.

Table 7-1 Prime Numbers under 100

2	3	5	7	11
13	17	19	23	29
31	37	41	43	47
53	59	61	67	71
73	79	83	89	97

Mersenne Primes

Mersenne Primes are special prime numbers that can be written as one less than a power of two. For example, $2^2 - 1 = 3$; $2^3 - 1 = 7$. Three and 7 are prime numbers, but 15 isn't a prime. So this formula doesn't always give you a prime, it's just that there are many primes that can be written this way.

In 1996, the Great Internet Mersenne Prime Search was launched. This involved a contest to find large Mersenne Primes. A gentleman, on his home computer, found a Mersenne Prime of sufficient size, and the Electronic Frontier Foundation awarded him $50,000. This foundation is offering $100,000 to the first person to discover a 10-million-digit number that is a Mersenne Prime. If you're interested, go to this site on the Internet: `www.mersenne.org`.

When you recognize that a number is prime, you don't waste time trying to find things to divide into it when you're reducing a fraction or factoring an expression. There are so many primes that you can't memorize or recognize them all, but just knowing or memorizing the primes smaller than 100 is a big help.

Composing composite numbers

Prime numbers are interesting to think about, but they can also be a dead end in terms of factoring algebraic expressions or reducing fractions. The opposite of prime numbers, com-posite numbers, can be broken down into factorable, reducible pieces. In this section, you'll see how.

Whole numbers larger than one that aren't prime are *compos-ite numbers* that can be broken down into the prime numbers that multiply together to give you that composite number. So, you can write every composite number as the product of prime numbers, a process known as *prime factorization*. Every number's prime factorization is unique.

Some examples of prime factorizations of composite numbers:

✔ $6 = 2 \cdot 3$

✔ $12 = 2 \cdot 2 \cdot 3 = 2^2 \cdot 3$

✔ $16 = 2 \cdot 2 \cdot 2 \cdot 2 = 2^4$

✔ $250 = 2 \cdot 5 \cdot 5 \cdot 5 = 2 \cdot 5^3$

✔ $510{,}510 = 2 \cdot 3 \cdot 5 \cdot 7 \cdot 11 \cdot 13 \cdot 17$

✔ $42{,}059 = 137 \cdot 307$

Okay, so the last one is a doozy. Finding that prime factoriza-tion without a calculator, computer, or list of primes is diffi-cult. The factors of some numbers aren't always obvious.

Writing Prime Factorizations

Writing the prime factorization of a composite number is one way to be absolutely sure you've left no stone unturned. These factorizations show you the one and only way a number can be factored.

A slick way of writing out prime factorizations is to do an upside-down division. You put a *prime factor* (a prime number that evenly divides the number you're working on) on the outside left and the result or *quotient* (the number of times it divides evenly) underneath. You divide the quotient (the number underneath) by another prime number and keep doing this until the bottom number is a prime. Then you can stop. The order you do this in doesn't matter. You get the same result or list of prime factors no matter what order you use.

Look at the prime factorization of 120:

$$2\,\underline{|120}$$
$$2\,\underline{|60}$$
$$2\,\underline{|30}$$
$$3\,\underline{|15}$$
$$5$$

Look at the numbers going down the left side of the work and the number at the bottom. They act the same as the divisors in a division problem. Only, in this case, they're all prime numbers. Although many composite numbers could have played the role of divisor for the number 120, the numbers for the prime factorization of 120 must be prime-number divisors.

When using this process, you usually do all the 2s first, then all the 3s, then all the 5s, and so on to make the prime factorization process easier, but you can do this in any order: $120 = 2 \cdot 2 \cdot 2 \cdot 3 \cdot 5 = 2^3 \cdot 3 \cdot 5$. In the next example, start with 13 because it seems obvious that it's a factor. The rest are all in a mixed-up order.

The prime factorization of 13,000:

$$13\,\underline{|13{,}000}$$
$$5\,\underline{|1{,}000}$$
$$2\,\underline{|200}$$
$$2\,\underline{|100}$$
$$5\,\underline{|50}$$
$$2\,\underline{|10}$$
$$5$$

So $13{,}000 = 13 \cdot 5 \cdot 2 \cdot 2 \cdot 5 \cdot 2 \cdot 5 = 2^3 \cdot 5^3 \cdot 13$

Getting Down to the Prime Factor

Doing the actual factoring in algebra is easier when you can recognize which numbers are composite and which are prime. If you know what they are, then you know what to do with them. Now, try putting all this knowledge to work!

Taking primes into account

Use prime factorization to reduce fractions. Start with numbers only and then add variables (letters that represent any real number) to the mix.

Reduce the fraction $\frac{120}{165}$ by following these steps:

1. **Find the prime factorization of the numerator.**

   120 is $2^3 \cdot 3 \cdot 5$

2. **Find the prime factorization of the denominator.**

   165 is $3 \cdot 5 \cdot 11$

3. **Next, write the fraction with the prime factorizations in it.**

   $$\frac{120}{165} = \frac{2^3 \cdot 3 \cdot 5}{3 \cdot 5 \cdot 11}$$

4. **Cross out the factors the numerator shares with the denominator to see what's left — the reduced form.**

   $$\frac{120}{165} = \frac{2^3 \cdot 3 \cdot 5}{3 \cdot 5 \cdot 11} = \frac{2^3 \cdot \cancel{3} \cdot \cancel{5}}{\cancel{3} \cdot \cancel{5} \cdot 11} = \frac{2^3}{11} = \frac{8}{11}$$

Now, try reducing the fraction $\frac{100}{243}$.

1. **Find the prime factorization of the numerator.**

   100 is $2^2 \cdot 5^2$

2. **Find the prime factorization of the denominator.**

   243 is 3^5

3. Write the fraction with the prime factorizations.

$$\frac{100}{243} = \frac{2^2 \cdot 5^2}{3^5}$$

Look at the prime factorizations. You can see that the numerator and denominator have absolutely nothing in common. The fraction can't be reduced. The two numbers are *relatively prime*. The beauty of using the prime factorization is that you can be sure that the fraction's reduction possibilities are exhausted — you haven't missed anything. You can leave the fraction in this factored form or go back to the simpler $\frac{100}{243}$. It depends on your preference.

Reduce the fraction $\frac{48x^3 y^2 z}{84xy^2 z^3}$.

1. Find the prime factorization of the numerator.

$$48x^3y^2z = 24 \cdot 3 \cdot x^3y^2z$$

2. Find the prime factorization of the denominator.

$$84xy^2z^3 = 22 \cdot 3 \cdot 7 \cdot xy^2z^3$$

3. Write the fraction with the prime factorization.

$$\frac{48x^3 y^2 z}{84xy^2 z^3} = \frac{2^4 \cdot 3 \cdot x^3 \cdot y^2 z}{2^2 \cdot 3 \cdot 7 \cdot xy^2 z^3}$$

4. Cross out the factors in common.

$$\frac{2^{\cancel{2}} \cdot \cancel{3} \cdot x^{\cancel{2}} \cancel{y^2} \cancel{z}}{\cancel{2^1} \cdot \cancel{3} \cdot 7 \cdot \cancel{xy^2} z^{\cancel{2}}} = \frac{4x^2}{7z^2}$$

By writing the prime factorizations, you can be certain that you haven't missed any factors that the numerator and denominator may have in common.

Pulling out factors — leaving the rest

Pulling out common factors from lists of terms or the sums or differences of a bunch of terms is done for a good reason. It's a common task when you're simplifying expressions and solving equations. The common factor that makes the biggest difference in these problems is the GCF, or greatest common factor. When you recognize the GCF and factor it out, it does the most good.

The *greatest common factor (GCF)* is the largest possible term that evenly divides each term of an expression containing two or more terms.

In any factoring discussions, the GCF, the most common and easiest factoring method, always comes up first. And it's helpful when solving equations. In an expression with two or more terms, finding the greatest common factor can make the expression more understandable and manageable.

The best case scenario is to recognize and pull out the GCF from a list of terms. Sometimes, though, the GCF may not be so recognizable. It may have some strange factors, such as 7, 13, or 23. It isn't the end of the world if you don't recognize one of these numbers as being a multiplier; it's just nicer if you do.

The three terms in the expression $12x^2y^4 + 16xy^3 - 20x^3y^2$ have common factors. What is the GCF? These steps help you find it:

1. **Determine any common numerical factors.**

   Each term has a coefficient that is divisible by a power of two, which is four.

2. **Determine any common variable factors.**

   Each term has x and y factors. The prime factorizations should help to show what the GCF is.

3. **Write the prime factorizations of each term.**

   $$12x^2y^4 = 2^2 \cdot 3 \cdot x^2y^4$$
   $$16xy^3 = 2^4 \cdot xy^3$$
   $$-20x^3y^2 = -2^2 \cdot 5 \cdot x^3y^2$$

   The GCF is the product of all the factors that all three terms have in common.

4. **Find the GCF.**

   The GCF contains the *lowest* power of each variable and number that occurs in any of the terms. Each variable in the sample problem has a factor of 2. If the lowest power of 2 that shows in any of the factors is 2^2, then 2^2 is part of the GCF.

Each factor has a power of x. If the lowest power of x that shows up in any of the factors is 1, then x^1 is part of the GCF.

Each factor has a power of y. If the lowest power of y that shows in any of the factors is 2, then y^2 is part of the GCF.

The GCF is $2^2xy^2 = 4xy^2$.

When finding the greatest common factor (GCF) of terms, the lowest power (exponent) of a particular factor that occurs in any of the terms determines the power of that factor in the GCF.

The GCF of $12x^2y^4 + 16xy^3 - 20x^3y^2$ is $4xy^2$.

5. **Divide each term by the GCF.**

The respective terms are divided as shown:

$$\frac{12x^2y^4}{4xy^2} = 3xy^2$$

$$\frac{16xy^3}{4xy^2} = 4y$$

$$\frac{-20x^3y^2}{4xy^2} = -5x^2$$

Notice that *all three* results of the division have nothing in common. The first two terms each have a y and the first and third each have an x, but nothing is shared by all the results. This is the best factoring result, which is what you want.

Rewrite the original expression with the GCF factored out and in parentheses:

$$12x^2y^4 + 16xy^3 - 20x^3y^2 = 4xy^2(3xy^2 + 4y - 5x^2)$$

Chapter 8

Sharing the Fun: Distributing

• •

In This Chapter

▶ Passing out the prize money evenly

▶ Multiplying binomials and trinomials

▶ Knowing what the same patterns look like

• •

*A*lgebra is full of contradictory actions. First you're asked to factor (see Chapter 9 for facts on factoring), and then distribute or "unfactor." In other words, first you're asked to reduce fractions, and then you're supposed to multiply and create bigger numbers. First you're asked to change a fraction to a decimal, and then a decimal to a fraction.

But rest assured that good reasons are behind doing all these seemingly contradictory processes. In this chapter, I tell you when, why, and how to factor and "unfactor." You want to make informed decisions and then have the skills to execute them correctly. What good does it do you to buy an airplane if you can't fly it?

Giving One to Each

When things are shared equally, everyone or everything involved gets an equal share — just one of the shares — not twice as many as others get. When a child is distributing her birthday treats to classmates, for example, it's "One for you, and one for you. . . ." In algebra, distributing is much the same process — each gets a share. *Algebraic distribution* means to multiply each of the terms within the parentheses by another term that is outside the parentheses.

To distribute a term over several other terms, multiply each of the other terms by the first. *Distribution* is multiplying each individual term in a grouped series of terms by a term outside of the grouping.

$$a(b + c) = a \times b + a \times c$$
$$a(b - c) = a \times b - a \times c$$

A term is made up of variable(s) and/or number(s) joined by multiplication and/or division. Terms are separated from one another by addition and/or subtraction.

1. **Multiply each term by the number(s) and/or variable(s) outside of the parentheses.**

   Distribute the number two over the terms in the parentheses.

   $$2(4x + 3y - 6) =$$
   $$2(4x) + 2(3y) - 2(6)$$

2. **Perform the multiplication operation in each term.**

   $$8x + 6y - 12$$

Now that you have the idea, try extracting a distribution operation out of the following scenario: At a particular car dealership, five salespersons, A, B, C, D, and E, sold 2, 8, 6, 5, and 9 cars last month, respectively. This is $2 + 8 + 6 + 5 + 9 = 30$ cars. The owner of the dealership wants to double the sales this month. He wants his sales force to sell a total of 60 cars. If each salesperson doubles what he sold last month, look at what happens.

1. **Multiply each term by the number(s) and/or variable(s) outside of the parentheses.**

   $$2(2 + 8 + 6 + 5 + 9) = 2(2) + 2(8) + 2(6) + 2(5) + 2(9)$$

2. **Perform the multiplication operation and add each term.**

   $$4 + 16 + 12 + 10 + 18 = 60 \text{ cars}$$

The answer is the same, of course, whether you distribute first or add up what's in the parentheses first. You have to make that judgment call. Distributing first to get the answer is the better choice when the multiplication of each term gives you nicer numbers. Adding up what's in the parentheses first, however, is preferred when the distributing gives you too many big multiplication problems. Sometimes it's easy to tell which case you have. At other times, you just have to guess and try it.

Distributing Signs

WARNING!

A positive (+) or a negative (-) sign is simple to distribute, but distributing a negative sign can cause errors. More contradictions!

Distributing positives

Distributing a positive sign makes no difference in the signs of the terms.

> ✔ $+ (4x + 2y - 3z + 7)$ is the same as multiplying through by $+1$.
>
> $$+1(4x + 2y - 3z + 7) = +1(4x) + 1(2y) + 1(-3z) + 1(7) = $$
> $$4x + 2y - 3z + 7$$

Even when a positive number other than the number one is distributed, it doesn't affect the signs.

> ✔ $+3 (4x + 2y - 3z + 7) = 3(4x) + 3(2y) + 3(-3z) + 3(7) = $
> $12x + 6y - 9z + 21$

It should come as no big surprise that the signs of the expression stay the same.

Distributing negatives

When distributing a negative sign, each term has a change of sign from negative to positive or from positive to negative.

Distribute a negative sign through a bunch of terms.

✔ $-(4x + 2y - 3z + 7)$ is the same as multiplying through by -1.

$$-1(4x + 2y - 3z + 7) = -1(4x) - 1(2y) - 1(-3z) - 1(7) =$$
$$-4x - 2y + 3z - 7$$

Change each term to the opposite sign.

One mistake to avoid when you're distributing a negative sign is not distributing over all the terms. This is especially the case when the process is hidden. By hidden, I mean that a negative sign may not be in front of the whole expression, where it sticks out. It can be between terms, showing a subtraction and not being recognized for what it is. Don't let the negative signs ambush you.

1. **Distribute the term.**

   $$4x(x - 2) - (5x + 3)$$

   Distribute the $4x$ over the x and the 2 by multiplying both terms by $4x$

   $$4x(x - 2) = 4x(x) - 4x(2)$$

2. **Distribute any negative sign.**

   Distribute the negative sign over the $5x$ and the 3 by changing the sign of each term. Be careful; a mistake can easily be made when the negative is distributed only over the $5x$.

3. **Multiply and combine the like terms.**

   $$4x(x) - 4x(2) - (+5x) - (+3) = 4x^2 - 8x - 5x - 3 =$$
   $$4x^2 - 13x - 3$$

Mixing It Up with Numbers and Variables

Distributing variables over the terms in an algebraic expression involves multiplication rules and the rules for exponents. When different variables are multiplied together, they can be written side by side without using any multiplication symbols. If the same variable is multiplied as part of the distribution, then the exponents are added together.

The exponent rule says that when multiplying exponents with the same base, add the exponents:

$$a^2 \cdot a^3 = a^5$$

The exponent rule for multiplying terms with the same base is used in the following problem.

1. **Distribute the term outside the parentheses over the terms within.**

   Multiply a through the expression $a^4 + 2a^2 + 3$.

   $$a(a^4 + 2a^2 + 3) = a \cdot a^4 + a \cdot 2a^2 + a \cdot 3$$

2. **Complete the multiplication.**

   $$a^5 + 2a^3 + 3a$$

And, again:

1. **Distribute the term outside the parentheses over the terms within.**

   Multiply a^3 through the expression $a^4 + 2a^2 + 3$

   $$a^3(a^4 + 2a^2 + 3) = a^3 \cdot a^4 + a^3 \cdot 2a^2 + a^3 \cdot 3$$

2. **Add the exponents.**

   $$a^{3+4} + 2a^{2+3} + a^3 \cdot 3$$

3. **Complete the distribution.**

   $$a^7 + 2a^5 + 3a^3$$

Adding exponents doesn't change just because there are negatives or fractions. For example: $4 + (-2) = 2$; $4 + (-4) = 0$; $4 + \frac{1}{3} = 4\frac{1}{3} = \frac{13}{3}$.

1. **Distribute the term outside the parentheses over those within.**

   Distribute the z^4 over each term.

   $$z^4(2z^2 - 3z^{-2} + z^{-4} + 5z^{1/3}) =$$
   $$z^4 \cdot 2z^2 - z^4 \cdot 3z^{-2} + z^4 \cdot z^{-4} + z^4 \cdot 5z^{1/3}$$

2. **Add the exponents.**

   $$2z^{4+2} - 3z^{4-2} + z^{4-4} + 5z^{4+1/3}$$

3. Complete the distribution.

$$2z^6 - 3z^2 + z^0 + 5z^{13/3} = 2z^6 - 3z^2 + 1 + 5z^{13/3}$$

The exponent zero means the value of the expression is one.

You combine exponents with different signs by using the rules for adding and subtracting signed numbers. Fractional exponents are combined after finding common denominators. Exponents that are improper fractions are left in that form.

Try going through many of the situations that could arise when distributing, such as distributing both a number and a variable, distributing various powers of more than one variable, distributing negatives, rewriting negative exponents as fractional terms, distributing fractional powers, and distributing radicals. This touches on just about anything you'd be apt to come across.

- Combine the variables by using the rules for exponents.

  Multiply each term by $5x$.

  $$5x(2x^2 + 3x - 4) = 5x \cdot 2x^2 + 5x \cdot 3x - 5x \cdot 4$$

  Multiply the numbers and the variables in each term.

  $$10x^3 + 15x^2 - 20x$$

- Combine the variables with the same base using the rules for exponents. The signs of the results follow the rules for multiplying signed numbers.

  $$-6y(5xy - 4x - 3y + 2)$$

  Multiply each term by $-6y$.

  $$-6y(5xy) - 6y(-4x) - 6y(-3y) - 6y(2)$$

  Do the multiplication in each term.

  $$-30xy^2 + 24xy + 18y^2 - 12y$$

- Notice that the last term in the next answer is the opposite of the term outside the parentheses. It is multiplied by the -1, which is the last term within the parentheses.

  $$5x^2y^3(16x^2 - 2x + 3xy + 4y^3 - 11y^5 + z - 1) =$$

  Multiply each term by $5x^2y^3$.

  $$5x^2y^3 \cdot 16x^2 - 5x^2y^3 \cdot 2x + 5x^2y^3 \cdot 3xy + 5x^2y^3 \cdot 4y^3 - 5x^2y^3 \cdot 11y^5 + 5x^2y^3 \cdot z - 5x^2y^3 \cdot 1$$

Complete the multiplication in each term. Add exponents where needed.

$$80x^4y^3 - 10x^3y^3 + 15x^3y^4 + 20x^2y^6 - 55x^2y^8 + 5x^2y^3z - 5x^2y^3$$

There are no like terms to be combined.

Distributing negative signs

Distribute the negative sign through, changing the signs to their opposites. Only the variables that are alike have exponential changes because the bases are the same.

✔ Look at the following problem, which is cluttered with negative signs.

$$-4xyzw(4 - x - y - z - w)$$

Multiply each term by $-4xyzw$.

$$-4xyzw(4) - -4xyzw(-x) - -4xyzw(-y) - -4xyzw(-z) - -4xyzw(-w)$$

Complete the multiplication in each term.

$$-16xyzw + 4x^2yzw + 4xy^2zw + 4xyz^2w + 4xyzw^2$$

✔ In this next example, the $-5x$ distributes over the first two terms. The $4x^2$ distributes over the second two terms.

$$-5x(3x + 2) + 4x^2(5 - 3x)$$

Distribute the two different factors.

$$-5x \cdot 3x - 5x \cdot 2 + 4x^2 \cdot 5 + 4x^2(-3x)$$

Multiply the individual terms.

$$-15x^2 - 10x + 20x^2 - 12x^3$$

The two terms with x^2 combine into one term.

$$-10x + 5x^2 - 12x^3$$

Negative exponents yield fractional answers

As the heading suggests, a base that has a negative exponent can be changed to a fraction. The base and the exponent become the denominator, but the exponent loses its negative sign in the process. Then cap it all off with a one in the numerator.

The formula for changing negative exponents to fractions is $a^{-n} = \dfrac{1}{a^n}$. See Chapter 4 for more details on negative exponents.

The following example shows you how a negative exponent can lead to a fraction.

➤ Distribute the $5a^{-3}b^{-2}$ over each term in the parentheses.

$$5a^{-3}b^{-2}(2ab^3 - 3a^2b^2 + 4a^4b - ab) =$$
$$5a^{-3}b^{-2}(2ab^3) - (5a^{-3}b^{-2})(3a^2b^2) + (5a^{-3}b^{-2})(4a^4b) - (5a^{-3}b^{-2})(ab)$$

Add the exponents.

$$10a^{-3+1}b^{-2+3} - 15a^{-3+2}b^{-2+2} + 20a^{-3+4}b^{-2+1} - 5a^{-3+1}b^{-2+1}$$

The factor of b with the 0 exponent becomes 1.

$$10a^{-2}b^1 - 15a^{-1}b^0 + 20a^1b^{-1} - 5a^{-2}b^{-1}$$

This next step shows the final result without negative exponents — using the formula for changing negative exponents to fractions, which is stated earlier in this section.

$$\frac{10b}{a^2} - \frac{15}{a} + \frac{20a}{b} - \frac{5}{a^2 b}$$

Working with fractional powers

Exponents that are fractions work the same way as exponents that are integers. They're added together. The only hitch is that the fractions have to have the same denominator to be added.

➤ Try the following distribution problem with exponents that are fractions to give yourself an idea of how to work through it.

$$x^{1/4}y^{2/3}(x^{1/2} + x^{3/4}y^{1/3} - y^{-1/3})$$

Distribute the $x^{1/4}y^{2/3}$.

$$x^{1/4}y^{2/3} \cdot x^{1/2} + x^{1/4}y^{2/3} \cdot x^{3/4}y^{1/3} - x^{1/4}y^{2/3} \cdot y^{-1/3}$$

Rearrange the variables and add exponents.

$$x^{1/4}x^{1/2}y^{2/3} + x^{1/4}x^{3/4}y^{2/3}y^{1/3} - x^{1/4}y^{2/3}y^{-1/3}$$

$$x^{1/4+1/2}y^{2/3} + x^{1/4+3/4}y^{2/3+1/3} - x^{1/4}y^{2/3-1/3}$$

Add the fractions.

$$x^{3/4}y^{2/3} + x^1y^1 - x^{1/4}y^{1/3}$$

REMEMBER

Radicals can be changed to expressions with fractions as exponents. This is handy when you want to combine terms with the same bases and you have some of the bases under radicals.

✔ $\sqrt{x} = x^{1/2}$

✔ $\sqrt{xy} = \sqrt{x}\sqrt{y} = x^{1/2}y^{1/2}$

✔ $\sqrt{x^3} = (x^3)^{1/2} = x^{3/2}$

Distribution is easier in this case if you first change everything to fractional exponents. (See more on exponential operations within radicals in Chapter 4.)

REMEMBER

The root of the radical becomes the denominator of the fractional exponent. For example: $\sqrt[n]{a} = a^{1/n}$ and $\sqrt[n]{a^m} = a^{m/n}$.

REMEMBER

The exponent rule for raising a product in parentheses to a power is to multiply each power in the parentheses by the outside power. For example: $(x^4y^3)^2 = x^8y^6$.

1. **Change the radical notation to fractional exponents.**

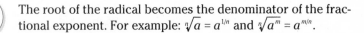

$$\sqrt{xy^3}\left(\sqrt{x^5y} - \sqrt{xy^7}\right) = (xy^3)^{1/2}\left[(x^5y)^{1/2} - (xy^7)^{1/2}\right]$$

2. **Raise the powers.**

$$x^{1/2}y^{3/2}[x^{5/2}y^{1/2} - x^{1/2}y^{7/2}]$$

3. **Distribute the outside term over each term within the parentheses.**

$$x^{1/2}y^{3/2}(x^{5/2}y^{1/2}) - x^{1/2}y^{3/2}(x^{1/2}y^{7/2})$$

4. **Add the exponents of the variables.**

$$x^{6/2}y^{4/2} - x^{2/2}y^{10/2}$$

5. **Simplify the fractions.**

$$x^3y^2 - x^1y^5$$

To *simplify* means to combine all that can be combined to put an expression in its most easily understood form.

In this example, the only thing accomplished is that the usual conventions of having the number first, followed by variables in alphabetical order, are observed.

✔ As you see, nothing combines in the following example.

$$(4 - 5x^2y + mnp)$$

Distribute $a^3b^4c^6$.

$$a^3b^4c^6(4) - a^3b^4c^6(5x^2y) + a^3b^4c^6(mnp)$$

Multiply each term.

$$4a^3b^4c^6 - 5a^3b^4c^6x^2y + a^3b^4c^6mnp$$

Distributing More than One Term

The preceding sections in this chapter describe how to distribute one term over several others. This section shows you how to distribute a binomial, a polynomial with two terms. You'll also discover how to distribute polynomials with three or more terms.

The word *polynomial* comes from poly meaning many, and nomen meaning name or designation. A *polynomial* is an algebraic expression with one or more terms in it. For example, a polynomial with one term is a monomial; a polynomial with two terms is a binomial. If there are three terms, it's a trinomial.

Distributing binomials

Distributing two terms, or a *binomial,* over several terms amounts to just applying the distribution process twice. The following steps tell you how:

1. **Break the first binomial into its two terms.**

   In this case, $(x^2 + 1)(y - 2)$, break the first binomial into its two terms, x^2 and 1.

The highest power in a polynomial

What is the highest power in a polynomial? The highest power of $x^3 + 1$, for example, is 3, so it's a *cubic binomial*. The word cubic tells you that the highest power is 3, and the word binomial tells you that the polynomial has a total of two terms, the x^3 and the 1. A *quintic polynomial* has a highest power of 5.

The following italicized words are listed alongside their corresponding powers. The phrases in parentheses that follow each word in the list can help you to remember and associate the word with the power that it refers to.

✔ First power: linear or *monic* (as in monogamy, for one wife)

✔ Second power: *quadratic* (quad, for a four-sided square)

✔ Third power: *cubic* (a sugar cube with three dimensions)

✔ Fourth power: *quartic* (four cups in a quart)

✔ Fifth power: *quintic* (quintuplets — five of them!)

✔ Sixth power: *sextic* (or, if this is too risqué, then use hexic)

✔ Seventh power: *septic* (as opposed to sewers — or, if you prefer, heptic)

✔ Eighth power: *octic* (eight-legged octopus)

✔ Ninth power: *nonic* (non-ic: not icky?)

✔ Tenth power: *decic* (as in decimal and decibel)

✔ Hundredth power: *hectic* (That's for sure!)

2. **Distribute each term of the first binomial over the other terms.**

    Distribute the first term, which is x^2, of first binomial $(x^2 + 1)$, over the second binomial, and distribute the second term, which is 1, of the first binomial over the second binomial.

$$x^2(y - 2) + 1(y - 2)$$

3. **Do the two distributions.**

$$x^2 (y - 2) + 1(y - 2) = x^2y - 2x^2 + y - 2$$

4. Simplify and combine any like terms.

In this case, nothing can be combined.

Now that you have the idea, try walking through a polynomial distribution that has variables in all the terms.

1. Break the first binomial into its two terms.

$$(a + b)(a^2 - ab + b^2)$$

Break the first binomial into its two terms to distribute it over the other terms.

2. Distribute each term of the first binomial over the other terms.

Distribute a and b over the other terms.

$$a(a^2 - ab + b^2) + b(a^2 - ab + b^2)$$

3. Do the two distributions.

$$a^3 - a^2b + ab^2 + a^2b - ab^2 + b^3$$

4. Simplify and combine any like terms.

Some terms can be combined. Note that the second and fourth terms are opposites and that the third and fifth terms are opposites.

$$a^3 + b^3$$

This simplifies nicely.

As you work through the example that follows, notice that the negative sign distributed over the last three terms and that the middle two terms combine.

1. Break the binomial into its two terms x^2 and $-y^2$.

$$(x^2 - y^2)(x^2 + 2xy + y^2)$$

2. Distribute each term of the binomial over the other terms.

$$x^2(x^2 + 2xy + y^2) - y^2(x^2 + 2xy + y^2)$$

3. Do the two distributions.

$$x^2(x^2) + x^2(2xy) + x^2(y^2) - y^2(x^2) - y^2(2xy) - y^2(y^2)$$

4. Simplify and combine any like terms.

Multiply and add exponents.

$$x^4 + 2x^3y + x^2y^2 - x^2y^2 - 2xy^3 - y^4$$

Combine terms.

$$x^4 + 2x^3y - 2xy^3 - y^4$$

Distributing trinomials

A *trinomial,* a polynomial with three terms, can be distributed over another expression. Each term in the first factor is distributed separately over the second factor, and then the entire expression is simplified, combining anything that can be combined.

The following problem introduces you to working through the distribution of trinomials.

1. Break the trinomial into its three terms *x, y,* and 2.

$$(x + y + 2)(x^2 - 2xy + y + 1)$$

2. Distribute each term of the trinomial over the other terms.

$$x(x^2 - 2xy + y + 1) + y(x^2 - 2xy + y + 1) + 2(x^2 - 2xy + y + 1)$$

3. Do the three distributions.

$$x^3 - 2x^2y + xy + x + x^2y - 2xy^2 + y^2 + y + 2x^2 - 4xy + 2y + 2$$

4. Simplify and combine any like terms.

$$x^3 - x^2y + 2x^2 + x - 2xy^2 + y^2 - 3xy + 3y + 2$$

Trinomial times a polynomial

This is where you can establish a rule that can cover just about any product of any number of terms. You can use this general method for four, five, or even more terms.

When distributing a polynomial (many terms) over any number of other terms, distribute each term in the first factor over all of the terms in the second factor. When the distribution is done, combine anything that goes together to simplify.

This example shows you how to multiply two trinomials.

1. **Separate the terms in the first factor from one another. Multiply each term in the first factor times the second factor.**

$$(x^2 + x + 2)(3x^2 - x + 1)$$

$$x^2(3x^2 - x + 1) + x(3x^2 - x + 1) + 2(3x^2 - x + 1)$$

2. **Distribute and do the multiplication.**

$$3x^4 - x^3 + x^2 + 3x^3 - x^2 + x + 6x^2 - 2x + 2$$

3. **Combine like terms.**

$$3x^4 + 2x^3 + 6x^2 - x + 2$$

Like the expression that results in the difference of two cubes, the problem that follows reuses the same two variables. Further, the first factor is a binomial, and the second factor is a trinomial. But this problem is a little different.

1. **Separate the terms in the first factor from one another. Multiply each term in the first factor times the second factor.**

$$(a^2 - b^2)(a^2 - ab - b^2)$$

$$a^2(a^2 - ab - b^2) - b^2(a^2 - ab - b^2)$$

2. **Distribute and do the multiplication.**

$$a^4 - a^3b - a^2b^2 - a^2b^2 + ab^3 + b^4$$

Notice the care taken when the second, negative factor of the binomial was multiplied through.

3. **Combine like terms.**

$$a^4 - a^3b - 2a^2b^2 + ab^3 + b^4$$

Making Special Distributions

Several distribution shortcuts can make life easier. Distributing binomials over other terms is not difficult, but you can save time if you recognize problems where you can apply a shortcut. If you don't notice that a special shortcut could have been used, don't worry about your oversight. But you may end up kicking yourself afterwards for not taking advantage of the easier process.

Recognizing the perfectly squared binomial

When the same binomial is multiplied by itself — when each of the first two terms is distributed over the second and same terms — then the resulting trinomial contains the squares of the two terms and twice their product:

$$(a + b)^2 = (a + b)(a + b) = a^2 + 2ab + b^2$$

✔ The result of the following operation is the sum of the squares of x and 3 along with twice their product.

$$(x + 3)(x + 3)$$

The square of x is x^2.

The square of 3 is 9.

Twice the product of x and 3 is $2(3x) = 6x$.

$$(x + 3)(x + 3) = x^2 + 6x + 9$$

Notice that the usual order of the terms was used: decreasing powers of x.

✔ Try the following binomial distribution with negative signs. Don't forget to square both the 4 and the y.

$$(4y - 5)(4y - 5)$$

The square of $4y$ is $16y^2$.

Note that the next square is positive.

The square of –5 is +25.

Twice the product of $4y$ and –5 is $2(4y)(-5) = -40y$.

So $(4y - 5)(4y - 5) = 16y^2 - 40y + 25$.

✔ In the following example, the terms are all variables.

$$(a^3 + b^2)(a^3 + b^2)$$

The square of a^3 is $(a^3)^2 = a^6$.

The square of b^2 is $(b^2)^2 = b^4$.

Twice the product of a^3 and b^2 is $2a^3b^2$.

So $(a^3 + b^2)(a^3 + b^2) = a^6 + 2a^3b^2 + b^4$.

✔ Parentheses group the last two terms together in this trinomial distribution.

$$[x + (a + b)][x + (a + b)]$$

The square of x is x^2.

The square of $(a + b)$ is $(a + b)^2 = a^2 + 2ab + b^2$.

Twice the product of x and $(a + b)$ is $2x(a + b)$.

$$[x + (a + b)][x + (a + b)] = x^2 + 2x(a + b) + a^2 + 2ab + b^2$$

If you want to further multiply this out, you can distribute that second term.

$$x^2 + 2xa + 2xb + a^2 + 2ab + b^2$$

Spotting the sum and difference of the same two terms

There's just one little — which can be big — difference between these multiplications and the ones in the previous section. The difference is that there's a sign change between the first and second binomials. If the sign between the two terms in the first binomial is positive, then in the second it's negative. The same two terms are always used — it's just that the sign between them changes.

The sum of any two terms multiplied by the difference of the same two terms is easy to spot and even easier to work out.

The sum of any two terms multiplied by their difference equals the difference of the squares of the same two terms. For any real numbers a and b:

$$(a + b)(a - b) = a^2 - b^2$$

Notice that the middle term just disappears because a term and its opposite are always in the middle. You can see that here:

$$(a + b)(a - b) = a(a - b) + b(a - b)$$

Distribute the a and b over the second factor.

$$a^2 - ab + ab - b^2 = a^2 - b^2$$

✔ The rule always works, so you can use the shortcut to do these special distributions.

$$(x - 4)(x + 4)$$

The first term squared is x^2.

The second term will always be negative and a perfect square like the first term.

$$(-4)(+4) = -16$$

So $(x - 4)(x + 4) = x^2 - 16$.

✔ Try the same easy process — multiplying the sum of two terms with their difference — again with a slightly more complicated variable term.

$$(ab - 5)(ab + 5)$$

The square of $ab = (ab)^2 = a^2b^2$.

The opposite of the square of $5 = -25$.

So $(ab - 5)(ab + 5) = a^2b^2 - 25$.

✔ The following example offers you a chance to work through the sum and difference of various groupings.

$$[5 + (a - b)][5 - (a - b)]$$

The square of $5 = 25$.

The opposite of the square of $(a - b) = -(a - b)^2$.

Square the binomial and distribute the negative sign.

$$-(a^2 - 2ab + b^2) = -a^2 + 2ab - b^2$$

So $[5 + (a - b)][5 - (a - b)] = 25 - a^2 + 2ab - b^2$.

Working out the difference between two cubes

So, what are cubes? Although some cubes are made of sugar and spice and everything nice, the cubes used in algebra are slightly different. Some of them are three-dimensional objects, but the cubes in this section are values that are multiplied times themselves — three times. Remember, a value multiplied by itself is a perfect square; a value multiplied by itself three times is a perfect cube. The variable x cubed is written x^3. For example, three cubed (3^3) is 27 because $3 \times 3 \times 3 = 27$.

An expression that results in the difference between two cubes is usually pretty hard to spot. You may not notice it until you get to the final answer and then say, "Oh, yeah. That's right!" However, being able to recognize what results in the difference of two cubes is even more important when you work on *cubic equations* (equations that contain a term with an exponent of three and no higher).

The difference of two cubes is equal to the difference of their cube roots times a trinomial, which contains the squares of the cube roots and the opposite of the product of the cube roots. For any real numbers a and b,

$$(a - b)(a^2 + ab + b^2) = a^3 - b^3$$

To recognize what distribution results in the difference of two cubes, look to see if the distribution has a binomial, $(a - b)$, which is the difference between two terms, times a trinomial, $(a^2 + ab + b^2)$, which has the squares of the two terms and the opposite their product.

A number's opposite is that same number with a different sign in front. If the number is a negative number, then its opposite would be positive and vice versa.

> ✔ Go ahead and distribute to see why this works.
>
> $$(a - b)(a^2 + ab + b^2)$$
>
> Distribute the a and the $-b$ over the trinomial.
>
> $$a(a^2 + ab + b^2) - b(a^2 + ab + b^2)$$
>
> Distribute the two values separately and multiply each term.
>
> $$a^3 + a^2b + ab^2 - a^2b - ab^2 - b^3$$
>
> Notice that the four terms in the middle are all pairs of opposites that add up to zero.
>
> Combine like terms.
>
> $$a^3 - b^3$$
>
> This pattern always results in the difference of two cubes.
>
> ✔ If you recognize the pattern in the following example, which has terms comprising known numbers and

multiple variables, then consider yourself an algebraic gold medalist!

$$(2 - ab)(4 + 2ab + a^2b^2)$$

The square of ab is $(ab)^2 = a^2b^2$, and the cube of ab is $(ab)^3 = a^3b^3$.

So $(2 - ab)(4 + 2ab + a^2b^2) = 8 - a^3b^3$.

Finding the sum of two cubes

This should look familiar. It's just like working out the result of the difference of two cubes, except that two signs change. The binomial has a plus sign and the middle term in the trinomial is minus.

$$(a + b)(a^2 - ab + b^2) = a^3 + b^3$$

When working with the two factors, the binomial and the trinomial, that give you the sum or difference of two cubes, the only difference in the factors is the two signs. The sign in the binomial is always the opposite of the sign in the middle of the trinomial. Look at what I mean in the following equations. The first result is the sum of two cubes, and the second result is the difference of two cubes.

$$(a + b)(a^2 - ab + b^2) = a^3 + b^3$$
$$(a - b)(a^2 + ab + b^2) = a^3 - b^3$$

Work through the following examples to give yourself a better understanding:

✔ The sign in the binomial is +, so the answer has a +. The cube of 4 is 64.

$$(x + 4)(x^2 - 4x + 16) = x^3 + 64$$

✔ The opposite of the product of 6 and $5yz$ is $-30yz$. The cube of $5yz = (5yz)^3 = 5^3y^3z^3$.

$$(6 + 5yz)(36 - 30yz + 25y^2z^2) = 216 + 125y^3z^3$$

TIP

Just as it's nice to have a list of perfect squares because they're used so much in algebra, it's equally nice to have a list of perfect cubes. You can always use your calculator to find the cube of a number, but it saves time if you already know it. Recognizing that a number is a perfect cube can come in handy later.

Try committing the list in Table 8-1 to memory.

Table 8-1	First Ten Perfect Cubes
$1^3 = 1$	$6^3 = 216$
$2^3 = 8$	$7^3 = 343$
$3^3 = 27$	$8^3 = 512$
$4^3 = 64$	$9^3 = 729$
$5^3 = 125$	$10^3 = 1,000$

Chapter 9

Factoring in the First Degree

* *

In This Chapter

▶ Taking away what all terms have in common

▶ Using variables versus numbers

▶ Finding the greatest common factor (GCF)

▶ Getting terms together

* *

*Y*ou may believe in the bigger-the-better philosophy, which can apply to salaries, cookies, or houses, but it doesn't really work for algebra. For the most part, the opposite is true: Smaller numbers are easier and more comfortable to deal with than larger numbers. In this chapter, you can discover how to get to those smaller-is-better terms. *First-degree terms* have a variable with an exponent of one. The factoring patterns you see here will carry over somewhat in higher degrees.

Factoring

Factoring is another way of saying: "Rewrite this so everything is all multiplied together." You usually start out with two or more terms and have to determine how to rewrite them so they're all multiplied together in some way or another. And, oh yes, the two expressions have to be equal!

Factoring out numbers

Before I start giving you rules and instructions on how to factor in algebra, you may want to see what the results of factoring look like. Take a look at the following examples, first:

Factoring is the opposite of distributing; it's "undistributing" (see Chapter 8 for more on distribution). In distribution, you multiply a series of terms by a common factor. Now, by factoring, you seek to find what a series of terms have in common and then take it away, dividing the common factor out from each term. Think of each term as a numerator and then find the same denominator for each. By factoring out, the common factor is put outside a parentheses or bracket and all the results of the divisions are left inside.

1. **Determine a common factor.**

   In the term $16a - 8b + 40c^2$, 2 is a common factor.

2. **Divide or "undistribute" each term by the common factor and write the results of the division in parentheses with the factor out in front.**

   In this example, this looks like $16a - 8b + 40c^2 = 2(8a - 4b + 20c^2)$.

3. **Determine whether you can factor out any other terms.**

   The terms left in the parentheses are still too big. They all still have something in common: 4. Factoring out 4, you get

   $$2(4[2a - b + 5c^2])$$

4. **Simplify your answer.**

   If you factor out a 4 after factoring out the 2, then the product of 4 and 2, which is 8, is the total amount you factored out:

   $$8(2a - b + 5c^2)$$

It's nice when you recognize going in that you can factor out a larger number, such as 8, but if it takes a couple steps to get to it, that's fine.

An expression can be written as the product of the largest number that divides all the terms evenly times the results of the divisions.

$$ab + ac + ad = a(b + c + d)$$

The following examples put this to practice:

✔ Stephen has 6 cats; Brad has 18 hamsters; Carlos has 16 parakeets; Donald has 4 dogs. These pet owners want to take their pets to various nursing homes to visit the residents, but they want to divide the animals into similar groups. How can they do this?

The sum of numbers representing the animals is 6 + 18 + 16 + 4, each of which can be divided evenly by 2. The 6 and 18 can be divided by 6, but the 16 and 4 cannot be divided by 6. The 16 and 4 can be divided by 4, but the 6 and 18 cannot be divided by 4.

Two is the biggest number that divides each evenly.

So these gentlemen can take two groups of animals to the nursing homes: 2(3 cats + 9 hamsters + 8 parakeets + 2 dogs). What a nice thing for them to do!

✔ Each of the terms in this example has a coefficient that is evenly divided by 3. The GCF (greatest common factor) of the numbers is 3, so a factor larger than 3 that can divide all the terms evenly is unavailable.

Factor $9x + 15y - 12z + 30$:

$$9x + 15y - 12z + 30 = 3(3x + 5y - 4z + 10)$$

The terms in the parentheses are the results of dividing each term by 3. Those terms don't have anything in common.

✔ Each term in the following example is divisible by six.

Factor $18a^2 - 24b - 36c + 42$:

$$18a^2 - 24b - 36c + 42 = 6(3a^2 - 4b - 6c + 7)$$

Relatively prime means that two terms have no prime factors in common. If the only factor that two numbers share in common is 1, then they're considered *relatively prime*.

For example, 1 is the only number that divides into both 18 and 25. Although neither 18 nor 25 is a prime number, they are *relatively prime*.

✔ The *proper* way to factor the following expression would be to write the prime factorization of each of the numbers and look for the GCF (greatest common factor).

What's really more practical and quicker in the end is to look for the biggest factor that *you can easily recognize.* Factor it out and then see if the numbers in the parentheses need to be factored again. Repeat the division until the terms in the parentheses are relatively prime.

$$450x + 540y - 486z + 216$$

Divide each term by two.

$$450x + 540y - 486z + 216 = 2(225x + 270y - 243z + 108)$$

The numbers in the parentheses are a mixture of odd and even, so you can't divide by 2 again. The numbers in the parentheses are all divisible by 3, but there's an even better choice.

You may have noticed that the digits in the numbers in all the terms add up to 9. That's the rule for divisibility by 9, so 9 can divide each term evenly. Thus,

$$2(225x + 270y - 243z + 108) = 2[9(25x + 30y - 27z + 12)]$$

Now multiply the 2 and 9 together to get

$$450x + 540y - 486z + 216 =$$
$$18(25x + 30y - 27z + 12)$$

You could have divided 18 into each term in the first place, but not many people know the multiplication table of 18. It's a stretch even for me.

Factoring out variables

Variables represent values; variables with exponents represent the powers of those same values. For that reason, variables as well as numbers can be factored out of the terms in an expression, and in this section you can find out how.

When factoring out powers of a variable, the smallest power that appears in any one term is the most that can be factored out. For example, in an expression such as $a^4b + a^3c + a^2d + a^3e^4$ the smallest power of a that appears in any term is the second power — a^2. So you can factor out a^2 from all the terms because a^2 is the GCF, the greatest common factor. You can't factor anything else out of each term.

$$a^4b + a^3c + a^2d + a^3e^4 = a^2(a^2b + a^1c + d + a^1e^4)$$

Diophantus

The mathematician Diophantus, the first to use symbols to abbreviate his thoughts systematically, lived some time between A.D. 100 and 400. Some consider him the Father of Algebra. Using symbols allowed him to categorize numbers of particular types and then symbolically study their properties. One of Diophantus's followers summarized his life in terms of an algebra riddle:

Diophantus's youth lasted one-sixth of his life. He grew a beard after one-twelfth more. After one-seventh more of his life, Diophantus married. Five years later he had a son. The son lived exactly one-half as long as his father, and Diophantus died just four years after his son. All this adds up to the years Diophantus lived.

Just in case you're dying to know the answer: Diophantus lived 84 years.

Two quick checks:

✔ Multiply through (distribute) your answer in your head to be sure that the factored form is equivalent to the original form.

$$a^2 \cdot a^2b + a^2 \cdot ac + a^2 \cdot d + a^2 \cdot ae^4 = a^4b + a^3c + a^2d + a^3e^4$$

✔ Another good way to check your work visually is to scan the terms in parentheses to make sure that they don't share the same variable.

Look at the following example of the quick checks. Pretend you just finished factoring the following problem:

$$x^2y^3 + x^3y^2z^4 + x^4yz = x^2y(y^2 + x^1y^1z^4 + x^2z)$$

Does your answer multiply out to become what you started with? Multiply in your head:

$$x^2y \cdot y^2 = x^2y^3 \quad \text{Check!}$$

$$x^2y \cdot xyz^4 = x^3y^2z^4 \quad \text{Check!}$$

$$x^2y \cdot x^2z = x^4yz \quad \text{Check!}$$

Those are the three terms in the original problem.

Now for the second part of the quick check. Look at what's in the parentheses of your answer. The first two terms have y and the second two have x and z, but no variable occurs in all three terms. Check!

Unlocking combinations of numbers and variables

The real test of the factoring process is combining numbers and variables, finding the GCF, and factoring successfully. Sometimes you may miss a factor or two, but a second sweep through can be done and is nothing to be ashamed of when doing algebra problems. If you do your factoring in more than one step, it really doesn't matter in what order you pull out the factors. You can do numbers first or variables first. It'll come out the same.

✔ Factor $12x^2y^3z + 18xy^2z^2 - 24xy^4z^3$.

The GCF is $6xy^2z$.

So $12x^2y^3z + 18x^3y^2z^2 - 24xy^4z^3 = 6xy^2z(2x^1y^1 + 3x^2z^1 - 4y^2z^2)$.

✔ The greatest common factor is 100 in the following example. Even though the powers of a and b are present in the first three terms, none of them occurs in the last term. So you're out of luck.

Factor $100a^4b - 200a^3b^2 + 300a^2b^2 - 400$.

So, doing the factorization,

$100a^4b - 200a^3b^2 + 300a^2b^2 - 400 = 100(a^4b - 2a^3b^2 + 3a^2b^2 - 4)$.

✔ The following expression cannot be factored. It's considered prime. Even though each of the numbers is composite (each can be divided by values other than themselves), they have no factors in common. The three terms share nothing.

Factor $26mn^3 - 25x^2y + 21a^4b^4mnxy$.

✔ In this example, you see that, even if you don't divide through by the GCF the first time, all is not lost. A second run takes care of the problem. Often, doing the factorizations in two steps is easier because the numbers you're dividing through by each time are smaller, and you can do the work in your head.

Factor $484x^3y^2 + 132x^2y^3 - 88x^4y^5$.

Assume that you determined that the GCF of the expression in this example is $4x^2y$.

Then $484x^3y^2 + 132x^2y^3 - 88x^4y^5 =$

$$4x^2y(121x^1y^1 + 33y^2 - 22x^2y^4).$$

Looking at the expression in the parentheses, you can see that each of the numbers is divisible by 11 and that there's a y in every term. The terms in the parentheses have a GCF (greatest common factor) of $11y$.

$$4x^2y[121x^2y^1 + 33y^2 - 22x^2y^4] =$$
$$4x^2y[11y(11x + 3y^1 - 2x^2y^3)] =$$
$$(4x^2y)(11y)(11x + 3y^1 - 2x^2y^3) =$$
$$44x^2y^2(11x + 3y^1 - 2x^2y^3)$$

You can do this factorization all at the same time, using the GCF $44x^2y^2$, but not everyone recognizes the multiples of 44 when they see them. Also, the factorization could have been done in two or more steps in a different order with different factors each time. The result always comes out the same in the end.

✔ Each term in the next example is negative; dividing out the negative from all the terms in the parentheses makes them positive.

Factor $-4ab - 8a^2b - 12ab^2$.

$$-4ab - 8a^2b - 12ab^2 = -4ab(1 + 2a^1 + 3b^1)$$

When factoring out a negative factor, be sure to change the signs of the terms.

Grouping Terms

Groups are formed when people have something in common with one another. Put 20 people on an island, leave them there for a few days, and chances are that the 20 people will form groups as they each seek out those they can relate to in some way.

The same general process can be done in factoring. The rules are a bit stricter than the preceding social situation, but the principle is the same. Find out what those algebraic principles are in this section.

When using grouping to factor:

1. **Divide the terms into groups of two terms in each.**

2. **Look for a greatest common factor (GCF) in each group of terms and factor.**

3. **Rewrite the expression in half as many terms. (This is what happens when you factor — you get half as many terms.)**

4. **Look for a GCF of the new terms. (If there isn't a GCF of the new terms, try a different arrangement of the terms in the divisions.)**

5. **Factor out the new GCF.**

Look at the following expression:

$$4xy + 4xb + ay + ab$$

You see that some terms have 4 in common. Some terms have x in common. And some terms have a, b, and y mixed in there, too. But all four terms do not have a variable or number in common. They can be grouped, though, into two parts that can be factored independently.

1. **Divide the terms into groups of two terms in each.**

   Group the first two terms together and then the last two.

   $$(4xy + 4xb) + (ay + ab)$$

2. **Look for a GCF in each group of terms and factor.**

   $$4xy + 4xb = 4x(y + b)$$

   $$ay + ab = a(y + b)$$

3. **Rewrite the expression in half as many terms.**

   $$4x(y + b) + a(y + b)$$

4. **Look for a GCF of the new terms.**

   The new GCF is $y + b$.

5. Factor out the new GCF.

$$(y + b)(4x + a)$$

This grouping business doesn't really help, though, unless the results of the two separate factorizations then share something. Looking at the preceding series of steps, in Step 3 each of the factored groups had $(y + b)$ in it. When this happens, the $(y + b)$ can be factored out of the newly formed terms.

$$4x(y + b) + a(y + b) = (y + b)(4x + a)$$

This is the factored form. If you multiply this through (distribute), then you get the four terms that you started with.

Again, the following example has nothing that all the terms share in common. But, if you group the first two and the last two, you can factor those pairs.

Factor $ax^2y - 3a + 9x^2y - 27$.

1. **Divide the terms into equal groups of two terms in each.**

$$(ax^2y - 3a) + (9x^2y - 27)$$

2. **Look for a GCF in each group of terms and factor.**

$$(ax^2y - 3a) = a(x^2y - 3)$$
$$(9x^2y - 27) = 9(x^2y - 3)$$

3. **Rewrite the expression in half as many terms.**

$$a(x^2y - 3) + 9(x^2y - 3) = (x^2y - 3)(a + 9)$$

4. **Look for a GCF of the new terms.**

The GCF is $x^2y - 3$.

5. **Factor out the new GCF.**

$$a(x^2y - 3) + 9(x^2y - 3) = (x^2y - 3)(a + 9)$$

What happens if the terms aren't in this order? How do you know what order to write them in? Do you get a different answer? Well, scramble the terms and write the problem as $ax^2y + 9x^2y - 27 - 3a$ and see what you have.

The first two terms have a GCF of x^2y. The second two terms have a GCF of –3. Grouping and factoring gives you $x^2y(a + 9) - 3(9 + a)$.

The expressions in the parentheses don't look exactly alike, but addition is *commutative* — you can add in either order and get the same result. You can reverse the 9 and the a in the last factor so that it looks the same as the first.

$$x^2y(a + 9) - 3(a + 9)$$

Now, you can factor the $(a + 9)$ out of each term to finish the problem.

$$(a + 9)(x^2y - 3)$$

The two factors in this answer are reversed from the first way you did the problem, but multiplication is also commutative.

In this last example, note that the two pairs of terms can be grouped and factored.

Factor $4ab^2 - 8ac^2 + 5x^2b - 10x^2c =$

$$(4ab^2 - 8ac^2) + (5x^2b - 10x^2c) =$$
$$4a(b^2 - 2c^2) + 5x^2(b - 2c)$$

The expressions in the parentheses look similar, but they aren't the same. Changing the order won't help in this case. There are now two terms, but they don't have a common factor. This expression is as simple as it can be. In other words, it's prime (in the algebraic sense).

Chapter 10

Getting the Second Degree

. . . .

In This Chapter

▶ Getting squared away with quadratic expressions

▶ Finding out how to FOIL without thwarting

▶ Stepping through the unFOIL process

▶ Getting organized to factor a quadratic

. . . .

Quadratic (second-degree) expressions, such as $3x^2 - 12$ or $-16t^2 + 32t + 11$, are studied extensively in algebra because they have so many applications in calculus and physics and other disciplines. These are expressions because they're made up of two or more terms with plus (+) or minus (−) signs between them. If there was an equal sign, they would be equations. The good news is that they're manageable. The bad news — well, there is none! Second-degree expressions are so darned nice to work with!

Quadratic expressions have a particular variable raised to the second degree. A quadratic expression can have one or more terms, and not all the terms must have a squared variable, but at least one of the terms needs to have that exponent of 2. Also, a quadratic expression can't have any power greater than 2. The highest power in an expression determines its name.

Some quadratic expressions may have one variable in them, such as $2x^2 - 3x + 1$. Others may have two or more variables, such as $2\pi r^2 + 2\pi rh$. They all have their place in mathematics and science. In this chapter, I show you how to make them work for you.

The Standard Quadratic Expression

The *standard quadratic, or second-degree, expression* has a variable that is squared, and no variables with powers higher than two in any of the terms. Where *a* is not equal to 0, quadratic expressions are of the form:

$$ax^2 + bx + c$$

You may notice that the following examples of quadratic expressions each have a variable raised to the second degree. There's no power higher than two in any of them.

$$4x^2 + 3x - 2$$
$$a^2 + 11$$
$$6y^2 - 5y$$

These expressions are usually written in terms of an *x, y, z,* or *w*. The letters at the end of the alphabet are used more frequently for the variable, while those at the beginning of the alphabet are usually used for a number or constant. This doesn't have to be the case, but it is usually the case.

In a quadratic expression, the *a* — the variable raised to the second power — can't be 0. If *a* was allowed to be 0, then the x^2 would be multiplied by 0. It wouldn't be a quadratic expression any more. The variables *b* or *c* can be 0, but *a* cannot.

Quadratics don't necessarily have all positive terms, either. The standard form, $ax^2 + bx + c$, is written with all positives for convenience. But if *a*, *b*, or *c* represents a negative number, then that term would be negative.

The terms are usually written with the second-degree term first, the first-degree term next, and the number last.

If an expression has more than one variable, decide which variable makes it a quadratic expression (look for the variable that's squared) and write the expression in terms of that variable. This means, after you find the variable that's squared,

write the rest of the expression in decreasing powers of that
variable.

$$aby + cdy^2 + ef$$

This can be a second-degree expression in y. Written in the
standard form for quadratics, $ax2 + bx + c$, where the second-
degree term comes first, it looks like

$$(cd)y^2 + (ab)y + ef$$

The parentheses aren't necessary in the preceding case and
don't change anything, but they're used sometimes for
emphasis. The parentheses just make seeing the different
parts easier.

Here's an example where you get to make choices:

$$a^2bx + cdx^2 + aef$$

Quadratic expressions you know

You're probably already familiar with
a few of these quadratic expressions
and equations:

- $E = mc^2$: Einstein said it first!
  This equation has only the one
  term because that's all old Al
  needed. The E stands for energy,
  m for mass, and the c is a constant
  representing the speed of light.

- $A = s^2$: You may have used this
  equation back in grade school.
  The area of a square is found by
  taking the length of a side and
  raising that number to the second
  degree. The A stands for the area
  and the s for the length of the side.

- $a^2 + b^2 = c^2$: This is Pythagoras's famous contribution to the
  understanding of the right triangle. a and b represent the lengths
  of the two shorter sides in a right
  triangle, and c represents the
  length of the hypotenuse — the
  longest side.

- $A = \pi r^2$: This is used to find the
  area of a circle. There's the argu-
  ment that "pi are squared" is
  wrong, because "pi are round" —
  sorry, couldn't resist that one.

These are just a few of the more
famous quadratic expressions and
equations. When you come across
them in real-life problems, you may
have to factor them on your way to
solving equations or answering questions involving them.

This can be a second-degree expression in terms of a or x.

Second degree in a: $(bx)a^2 + (ef)a + cdx^2$

Even though there's a second-degree factor of x in the last term, that term is thought of as a constant, a value that doesn't change, rather than a variable if the expression is a to the second degree.

Now, changing roles, the second degree in x: $(cd)x^2 + (a^2b)x + aef$.

Reining in Big Numbers

Some perfectly good quadratic expressions are just too awkward to handle. Some can be made better by factoring. Some are just going to be uncooperative — you're stuck with them. In this section, I go back to my favorite standby: finding a greatest common factor. If the terms in the quadratic have something in common, then that can be factored out, leaving something more reasonable to deal with.

✓ The following quadratic operation can be made more useable by factoring out the common factor and arranging the result in a nice, organized expression:

$$800x^2 + 40,000x - 100,000$$

It has large numbers, but each number can be evenly divided by 800 — a common factor.

$$800x^2 + 40,000x - 100,000 =$$
$$800(x^2 + 50x - 125)$$

✓ The following quadratic operation has four different variables with powers of 2. Only the x, though, appears in a term with a power of 1. So, you may choose to write this as a quadratic in x and factor out some of the other variables.

$$a^2x^2 + a^2c^2 + a^2b^2x$$

Rewrite the expression in decreasing powers of x.

$$a^2x^2 + a^2b^2x + a^2c^2$$

Find the GCF, which is a^2, and factor it out.

$$a^2(x^2 + b^2x + c^2)$$

FOILing

FOIL is an acronym for first, outer, inner, and last. It cropped up somewhere between my high school years and my teaching years. It was sort of "under the counter" at first. Respected mathematicians didn't want to use it. But it has caught on and is now accepted, published, and used extensively in the algebra classroom. FOIL is easy to remember and apply.

This chapter is on factoring, but first you need to find out how to multiply two binomials together using FOIL. Chapter 8 shows you how to multiply two binomials together by distributing. This chapter gives you an alternate method.

FOILing basics

Many quadratic expressions, such as $6x^2 + 7x - 3$, are the result of multiplying two *binomials* (two terms separated by addition or subtraction) together, so you can undo the multiplication by factoring them.

$$6x^2 + 7x - 3 = (2x + 3)(3x - 1)$$

The right side is the factored form. But how can you tell that the left side of that equation is equal to the right side just looking at it? It's not like a greatest common factor, when you look for something in common.

What does FOIL stand for? The letters each refer to two terms — one from each of two binomials — multiplied together in a certain order. The steps don't have to be done in this order, but they usually are. Otherwise, the acronym would be something like OFIL (heaven forbid). The following list describes what each letter in the FOIL acronym stands for:

- ✔ **F** stands for the first term in each binomial: $(\mathbf{3a} + 6)(\mathbf{2a} - 1)$
- ✔ **O** stands for the two outermost terms — those farthest to the left and right: $(\mathbf{3a} + 6)(2a - \mathbf{1})$
- ✔ **I** stands for the inner terms in the middle: $(3a + \mathbf{6})(\mathbf{2a} - 1)$
- ✔ **L** stands for the last term in each binomial: $(3a + \mathbf{6})(2a - \mathbf{1})$

In each binomial, there's the left term and the right term. But the two terms have other names, also. (Just like someone named Michael may be "Mike" to one person and "son" to another.) The other names for the terms in the binomials refer to their positions in terms of the whole picture. The two terms not in the middle are the outer terms. The two terms in the middle are the inner terms. Use this as an example: $(a + b)$ $(c + d)$. The terms a and c are first; the terms b and d are last in each binomial. The terms a and d are outer; the terms b and c are inner in the big picture. As you can see, each term has two names. In the problem $(2x + 3)(3x - 1)$ the term $2x$ is called *first* one time and *outer* another time. That's okay.

Figure 10-1 gives you a visual on how this is done.

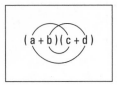

Figure 10-1: The FOIL happy face.

FOILed again, and again

The following steps demonstrate how to use FOIL on a multiplication problem: $(2x + 3)(3x - 1)$.

1. **Multiply the first term of each binomial together.**

   $$(2x + 3)(3x - 1)$$
   $$(2x)(3x) = 6x^2$$

2. **Multiply the outer terms together.**

   $$(2x + 3)(3x - 1)$$
   $$(2x)(-1) = -2x$$

3. **Multiply the inner terms together.**

   $$(2x + 3)(3x - 1)$$
   $$(3)(3x) = 9x$$

4. Multiply the last term of each expression together.

$$(2x + 3)(3x - 1)$$
$$(3)(-1) = -3$$

5. List the four results of FOIL in order.

$$6x^2 - 2x + 9x - 3$$

6. Combine the like terms.

$$6x^2 + 7x - 3$$

Distributing the two terms in the first binomial over the second produces the same result, but in the case of binomials, using FOIL is easier. For more on distributing, see Chapter 8.

See how the FOIL numbered steps work on a couple of negative terms in the following example:

$$(x - 3)(2x - 9)$$

1. Multiply the first terms.

$$(x)(2x) = 2x^2$$

2. Multiply the outer terms.

$$(x)(-9) = -9x$$

3. Multiply the inner terms.

$$(-3)(2x) = -6x$$

4. Multiply the last terms.

$$(-3)(-9) = 27$$

5. List the four results of FOIL in order.

$$2x^2 - 9x - 6x + 27$$

6. Combine the like terms.

$$2x^2 - 15x + 27$$

The following example is a bit more complicated to do, but FOIL makes it much easier. The tasks are broken down into smaller, simpler tasks, and then the results are combined for the final result.

The next steps take you through $[x + (y - 4)][3x + (2y + 1)]$.

Carl Friedrich Gauss, child prodigy

The mathematician Carl Friedrich Gauss, a child prodigy, was only 3 years old when he corrected some calculations in his father's payroll records. He went on to make significant contributions to mathematics.

Legend has it that when Gauss was a schoolboy, his tired teacher told the class to find the sum of the numbers from 1 through 100 to keep them occupied so he could rest. Moments later, little Carl Friedrich was at the teacher's elbow with a solution. The teacher looked in disbelief at the boy's answer, which, of course, was correct. Gauss wasn't a whiz at adding. He just got organized and found patterns in the numbers to make the adding easier and much more interesting. He saw that 1 + 99 = 100, 2 + 98 = 100, 3 + 97 = 100, and so on. The sum of 49 of these 100s, the 50 in the middle, and the 100 at the end is 5,050.

Thanks to Gauss, a standard formula is available for the sum of any list of consecutive integers. This formula is $S = n(n + 1) \div 2$. The S represents the sum of the numbers, and the n is the biggest, or last, number in the list that starts with the number 1.

1. **Multiply the first terms.**

$$(x)(3x) = 3x^2$$

2. **Multiply the outer terms.**

$$(x)(2y + 1) = 2xy + x$$

3. **Multiply the inner terms.**

$$(y - 4)(3x) = 3xy - 12x$$

4. **Multiply the last terms. The last terms are two binomials, too. You FOIL these binomials when you finish this series of FOIL steps.**

$$(y - 4)(2y + 1)$$

5. **List the four results of FOIL in order.**

$$3x^2 + 2xy + x + 3xy - 12x + (y - 4)(2y + 1)$$

6. **Combine like terms.**

$$3x^2 + 5xy - 11x + (y - 4)(2y + 1)$$

Notice the product of two binomials from the preceding Step 4: $(y - 4)(2y + 1)$. You can FOIL them.

1. **Multiply the first terms:** $(y)(2y) = 2y^2$

2. **Multiply the outer terms:** $(y)(1) = y$

3. **Multiply the inner terms:** $(-4)(2y) = -8y$

4. **Multiply the last terms:** $(-4)(1) = -4$

5. **Write the results in order:** $2y^2 + y - 8y - 4$

6. **Combine like terms:** $2y^2 - 7y - 4$

   Now, replace the two binomials multiplied together with this new result, and you can rewrite the entire problem.

$$3x^2 + 5xy - 11x + 2y^2 - 7y - 4$$

UnFOILing

When you look at an expression such as $2x^2 - 5x - 12$, you may think that figuring out how to factor this into the product of two binomials is an awful chore. And you may wonder whether it even can be factored that way. Let me assure you that these problems are really quite easy.

The nice thing is that there's a system to make unFOILing simple. You go through the system, and it helps you find what the answer is or helps you determine if there isn't an answer. This can't be said about all factoring problems, but it is true of quadratics in the form $ax^2 + bx + c$. That's why quadratics are so nice to work with in algebra.

The key to unFOILing these factoring problems is being organized.

- ✔ Be sure you have an expression in the form $ax^2 + bx + c$.

- ✔ Be sure the terms are written in the order of decreasing powers.

- ✔ If needed, review the lists of prime numbers and perfect squares (refer to Chapters 7 and 8).

- ✔ Follow the steps.

Follow these steps to factor the quadratic $ax^2 + bx + c$, which is written in the order of decreasing powers, using unFOIL.

1. **Determine all the ways you can multiply two numbers to get *a*.**

   Every number can be written as at least one product, even if it's only the number times one. So assume that there are two numbers, *e* and *f*, whose product is equal to *a*: $a = e \cdot f$. These are the two numbers you want for this problem.

2. **Determine all the ways you can multiply two numbers together to get *c*.**

   If the value of *c* is negative, ignore the negative sign for the moment. Concentrate on what factors result in the absolute value of *c*.

   Now assume that there are two numbers, *g* and *h*, whose product is equal to *c*: $c = g \cdot h$. Use these two numbers for this problem.

3. **Now look at the sign of *c* and your lists from Steps 1 and 2.**

   1. If *c* is positive, find a value from your Step 1 list and another from your Step 2 list such that the sum of their product and the product of the two remaining numbers in those steps results in *b*.

      Assume, using $e \cdot f$ and $g \cdot h$, that $e \cdot g + f \cdot h = b$.

   2. If *c* is negative, find a value from your Step 1 list and another from your Step 2 list such that the difference of their product and the product of two remaining numbers from those steps results in *b*.

      Assume, using $e \cdot f$ and $g \cdot h$, that $e \cdot g - f \cdot h = b$.

4. **Arrange your choices as binomials.**

   The *e* and *f* have to be in the first positions in the binomials, and the *g* and *h* have to be in the last positions. They have to be arranged so the multiplications in Step 3 have the correct outer and inner products.

   $$(e\ h)\ (f\ g)$$

5. **Place the signs appropriately.**

   The signs are both positive if *c* is positive and *b* is positive.

The signs are both negative if c is positive and b is negative.

One sign is positive and one negative if c is negative; the choice depends on whether b is positive or negative and how you arrange the factors.

Using unFOIL, follow these steps to factor the quadratic $2x^2 - 5x - 12$, which is in the form $ax^2 + bx + c$ and written in the order of decreasing powers.

1. **Determine all the ways you can multiply two numbers to get a.**

   You can get these numbers from the prime factorization of a. See Chapter 7 if you need to review prime factorizations.

    Prime numbers can only be divided by themselves and 1. Prime factorization is finding the prime numbers that divide any given value.

   Sometimes, writing out the list of ways to multiply is a big help.

   In the example $2x^2 - 5x - 12$, the value of a is 2. The only way to multiply two numbers together to get 2 is 1×2.

2. **Determine all the ways you can multiply two numbers to get c.**

   Again, referring to the example, $2x^2 - 5x - 12$, the value of c is -12. Ignore the negative sign right now. The negative becomes important in the next step. Just concentrate on what multiplies together to give you 12.

   There are three ways to multiply two numbers together to get 12: 1×12, 2×6, and 3×4.

3. **Look at the sign of c and your lists from Steps 1 and 2.**

   1. If c is positive, find a value from your Step 1 list and another from your Step 2 list such that the sum of their product and the product of the two remaining numbers in those steps results in b.

   2. If c is negative, find a value from your Step 1 list and another from your Step 2 list such that the difference of their product and the product of two remaining numbers from those steps results in b.

    4. Choose a product from Step 1 and a product from Step 2.

In the case of the example, c is -12 and b is 5. So, look for a combination from Step 1 and Step 2 whose difference results in 5.

Use the 1×2 from Step 1 and the 3×4 from Step 2. Multiply the 1 from Step 1 times the 3 from Step 2 and then multiply the 2 from Step 1 times the 4 from Step 2.

$$(1)(3) = 3 \text{ and } (2)(4) = 8$$

The two products are 3 and 8, whose difference is 5.

$$8 - 3 = 5.$$

    5. Arrange your choices as binomials so the results are those you want.

From the example, the following arrangement multiplies the $(1x)(2x)$ to get the $2x^2$ needed for the first product. Likewise, the 4 and 3 multiply to give you 12. The outer product is $3x$ and the inner product is $8x$.

$$(1x\ 4)(2x\ 3)$$

    6. Place the signs to give the desired results.

$$(1x - 4)(2x + 3) = 2x^2 - 5x - 12$$

This next example, $24x^2 - 34x - 45$, offers many numbers to choose from.

    1. Determine all the ways you can multiply two numbers to get a.

a is 24, which equals 1×24, 2×12, 3×8, or 4×6.

    2. Determine all the ways you can multiply two numbers to get c.

c is 45, which equals 1×45, 3×15, or 5×9.

    3. Look at the sign of c and your lists from Steps 1 and 2 to see if you want a sum or difference.

c is negative, so you want a difference of 34 between products.

    4. Choose a product from Step 1 and a product from Step 2.

Use the 4×6 from a and the 5×9 from c. The product of 4 and 5 is 20. The product of 6 and 9 is 54. The difference of these products is 34.

5. **Arrange your choices as binomials so the results are those you want.**

   $(4x\ 9)(6x\ 5)$ line up products the way you want.

6. **Place the signs to give the desired results.**

   $$(4x - 9)(6x + 5) = 24x^2 - 34x - 45$$

The combinations you want may not just leap out at you. But having a list of all the possibilities helps heaps. You can start systematically trying out the different combinations. For instance, take the 1×24 and try it with all three sets of numbers that give you c: 1×45, 3×15, or 5×9. If none of those work, then try the 2×12 with all the sets of numbers that give you c. Continue until you've systematically gone through all the possible combinations. If none works, you know you're done. Doing it this way doesn't leave you wondering if you've missed anything.

This last example, $18x^2 - 27x - 4$, looks, at first, like a great candidate for factoring by this method. You'll see, though, that not everything can factor. Also, the point can be made that using this method assures you that you've "left no stone unturned."

1. **Determine all the ways you can multiply two numbers to get a.**

   The 18 can be written as 1×18 or 2×9 or 3×6.

2. **Determine all the ways you can multiply two numbers to get c.**

   The 4 can be written as 1×4 or 2×2.

3. **Look at the sign of c and your lists from Steps 1 and 2 to see if you want a sum or difference.**

   The last term is negative, so you want the difference of the products to be 27.

4. **Choose a product from Step 1 and a product from Step 2.**

   You can't seem to find any combination that gives you a difference of 27. Run through them to be sure that you haven't missed anything.

Using the 1×18, cross it with:

1×4 gives you a difference of either 14, using the (1)(4) and (18)(1) or 71 using the (1)(1) and the (18)(4).

2×2 gives you a difference of 34 using (1)(2) and (18)(2); there's only one choice because both of the second factors are 2.

Using the 2×9, cross it with:

1×4 gives you a difference of either 34 using (2)(1) and (9)(4) or 1, using (2)(4) and (9)(1).

2×2 gives you a difference of 14, only.

Using the 3×6, cross it with:

1×4 gives you a difference of either 21, using (3)(1) and (6)(4), or 6, using (3)(4) and (6)(1).

2×2 gives you a difference of 6, only.

Because you exhausted all the possibilities and have not been able to create a difference of 27, you can assume that this quadratic cannot be factored. It is *prime*.

Factoring Several Expressions

Sometimes you have to factor a problem more than once. This section shows you how two completely different factoring techniques can be used on the same problem. The process of using different factoring techniques is different from reusing the same methods, such as taking out common factors several times.

A quadratic, such as $40x^2 - 40x - 240$, can be factored using two different techniques, which can be done in two different orders, making the problem easier and harder. It's the order in which the factoring is done that makes one way easier and the other way harder.

I'll show you the harder method first, so you'll see why it's important to make a good choice. In this case, the big numbers are left in and the unFOILing is done first.

1. **Determine all the ways you can multiply two numbers to get *a*.**

   The 40 can be written as 1×40, 2×20, 4×10, or 5×8.

2. **Determine all the ways you can multiply two numbers to get *c*.**

   The 240 can be written as 1×240, 2×120, 3×80, 4×60, 5×48, 6×40, 8×30, 10×24, 12×20, or 15×18.

3. **Look at the sign of *c* and your lists from Steps 1 and 2.**

   The last term is negative, so you want the *difference* of the products to be 40.

   Use the 4×10 and the 12×20, multiply $(4)(20)$ to get 80, and multiply $(12)(10)$ to get 120. The difference between 80 and 120 is 40.

4. **Arrange your choices as binomials and place the signs appropriately.**

   $$(4x - 12)(10x + 20) = 40x^2 - 40x - 240$$

   But just look at those binomials. Each of them can be factored themselves. The terms in the first binomial can each be factored by 4, and the terms in the second binomial can each be factored by 10.

   $$(4x - 12)(10x + 20) = 4(x - 3)10(x + 2) = 40(x - 3)(x + 2)$$

Next, try the easier way. Factor out the greatest common factor (GCF), first.

$$40x^2 - 40x - 240 = 40(x^2 - x - 6)$$

1. **Just look inside the parentheses.**

   The 1 can be written only as 1×1. The 6 can be written as 1×6 or 2×3. Notice how the list of choices is much shorter and more manageable than if you try to unFOIL before factoring out the GCF.

2. **Looking at the sign of *c*, choose your products.**

   The last term is negative, so you want the difference of the products to be 1. Using the 1×1 and the 2×3, it's easy to set up the factors:

   $$(1x \quad 2)(1x \quad 3)$$

The middle term, x, is negative, so you want the $3x$, the outer terms, to be negative. Put the 40 that you factored out in the first place back into the answer.

$$40x^2 - 40x - 240 = 40(x - 2)(x - 3)$$

You can get to the correct answer no matter what you choose to do in what order. As a general rule, though, it's usually best to factor out a GCF first.

Chapter 11

Factoring Special Cases

· ·

In This Chapter

▶ Paring down perfect cubes

▶ Sorting out the difference of two squares

▶ Summing up two perfect cubes

▶ Putting polynomials with several terms in order

· ·

*T*his chapter has some mighty helpful factoring information that doesn't belong under linear or quadratic factoring rules. You may want to look at Chapters 9 and 10 for more factoring rules and tips. Half of the factoring process is knowing the rules and the other half is recognizing when to use what rule. These are equally important skills — you need both.

Befitting Binomials

If a binomial (two-term) expression can be factored at all, it must be factored in one of four ways. First, look at the addition or subtraction sign that always separates the two terms within a binomial. Then look at the two terms. Are they squares? Are they cubes? Are they nothing special at all? The nice thing about having two terms in an expression is that you have four and only four ways to check.

The four ways to factor a binomial are

✔ Finding the greatest common factor (GCF)

✔ Factoring the difference of two perfect squares

✔ Factoring the difference of two perfect cubes

✔ Factoring the sum of two perfect cubes

When you have a factoring problem with two terms, you can go through the list to see which way works. Sometimes the two terms can be factored in more than one way, such as finding the GCF and the difference of two squares. After you go through one factoring method, check inside the parentheses to see if another factoring can be done. If you checked each item on the list of ways to factor and none works, then you know that the expression can't be factored any further. You can stop looking and say you're done.

Finding the greatest common factor (GCF) is always an easy and quick option to look into when factoring: (For more on how to find the GCF, see Chapter 9.) What's left after factoring is much easier to deal with. But do read the following sections to discover other factoring pearls of wisdom.

Factoring the difference of two perfect squares

If two terms in a binomial are perfect squares and they're separated by subtraction, then they can be factored. A perfect square is not a reference to that ol' high school prom date with two left feet who refused to dance the entire evening. A perfect square is the result of multiplying another number by itself. Twenty-five is a perfect square because it's equal to 5 times 5. To factor one of these binomials, just find the square roots of the two terms that are perfect squares and write the factorization as the sum and difference of the square roots. For example, $x2 - y2 = (x + y)(x - y)$. However, looking at another example, the binomial $x^2 + 3$ is not the difference of two perfect squares because there's a plus sign, not a minus, and 3 isn't a perfect square.

If subtraction separates two squared terms, then the sum and difference of the two square roots factors the binomial.

$$a^2 - b^2 = (a + b)(a - b)$$

✔ Factor $9x^2 - 16$. The square roots of $9x^2$ and 16 are $3x$ and 4, respectively. The sum of the roots is $3x + 4$ and the difference between the roots is $3x - 4$. So $9x^2 - 16 = (3x + 4)(3x - 4)$.

✔ Factor $25z^2 - 81y^2$. The square roots of $25z^2$ and $81y^2$ are $5z$ and $9y$, respectively. So $25z^2 - 81y^2 = (5z + 9y)(5z - 9y)$.

✔ Factor $x^4 - y^6$. The square roots of x^4 and y^6 are x^2 and y^3, respectively. So $x^4 - y^6 = (x^2 + y^3)(x^2 - y^3)$.

✔ Factor $x^2 - 3$. In this case, the second number is not a perfect square. But sometimes it's preferable to have the expression factored, anyway. The square root of x^2 is x, and you can write the square root of 3 as $\sqrt{3}$. (For more on square roots and radicals, see Chapter 4.) Now the factorization can be written: $x^2 - 3 = (x + \sqrt{3})(x - \sqrt{3})$.

Factoring the difference of perfect cubes

A perfect cube is the number you get when you multiply a number times itself then multiply the answer times the first number again. A cube is the third power of a number. The difference of two cubes is a binomial expression, $a^3 - b^3$.

The most well-known perfect cubes are those whose roots are integers, not decimals. Becoming familiar with and recognizing these cubes in an algebra problem can save you time and improve your accuracy.

Refer to Chapter 4 if these rules for working with exponents don't ring a bell. In the first example, the cube outside the parentheses means each variable gets raised to that power. In the second example, the rule involving raising a power to a power is used. Both results are cubes.

$$(yz)^3 = y^3 \times z^3$$

$$(a^2)^3 = a^6$$

Variable cubes are relatively easy to spot because their exponents are always divisible by 3. When a number is cubed and multiplied out, you can't always tell it's a cube unless you memorize the cubes or refer to lists.

Look at the following list. These expressions are the difference of cubes that can be factored. Each term is a cube — the numbers all have a cube root (the number that's multiplied by itself three times), most of which are on the list of cubes. The variables all have powers that are multiples of 3.

- $m^3 - 8$
- $1{,}000 - 27z^3$
- $64x^6 - 125y^{15}$

Notice that every number is a perfect cube and that every variable has a power that is a multiple of 3.

To factor the difference of two perfect cubes, remember that the difference of two perfect cubes equals the difference of their cube roots multiplied by the sum of their squares and the product of their cube roots.

$$a^3 - b^3 = (a - b)(a^2 + ab + b^2)$$

The results of factoring the difference of perfect cubes are

- A binomial factor $(a - b)$ made up of the two cube roots of the perfect cubes separated by a minus sign. If the cube isn't there, and the number is smaller than the largest cube on the list, then the number isn't a perfect cube. For bigger numbers, use a scientific calculator and the cube root button.

- A trinomial factor $(a^2 + ab + b^2)$ made up of the squares of the two cube roots added to the product of the cube roots in the middle. Remember, a trinomial has three terms, and this one has all plus signs in it.

The following three examples show you how the rule works.

- Factor $m^3 - 8$.

    The cube root of m^3 is m, and the cube root of 8 is 2.

    $$m^3 - 8 = (m - 2)(m^2 + 2m + 4)$$

    Notice that the sign between the m and the 2 is the same as the sign between the cubes. The square of m is m^2 and the square of 2 is 4. The product of the two cube roots is $2m$, and the signs in the trinomial are all positive.

- Factor $64x^3 - 27y^6$.

    The cube root of $64x^3$ is $4x$, and the cube root of $27y^6$ is $3y^2$.

The square of $4x$ is $16x^2$, the square of $3y^2$ is $(3y^2)^2 = 9y^4$, and the product of $(4x)(3y^2)$ is $12xy^2$.

$$64x^3 - 27y^6 = (4x - 3y^2)(16x^2 + 12xy^2 + 9y^4)$$

✔ Factor $a^3b^6c^9 - 1{,}331d^{300}$.

The cube root of $a^3b^6c^9$ is ab^2c^3, and the cube root of $1{,}331d^{300}$ is $11d^{100}$.

The square of ab^2c^3 is $a^2b^4c^6$, and the square of $11d^{100}$ is $121d^{200}$. The product of $(ab^2c^3)(11d^{100})$ is $11ab^2c^3d^{100}$.

$$a^3b^6c^9 - 1{,}331d^{300} =$$
$$(ab^2c^3 - 11d^{100})(a^2b^4c^6 + 11ab^2c^3d^{100} + 121d^{200})$$

Factoring the sum of perfect cubes

You have a break coming. The rule for factoring the sum of two perfect cubes is almost the same as the rule for factoring the difference between perfect cubes, which I cover in the previous section. You just have to change two little signs to make it work.

The sum of two cubes equals the sum of its roots times the squares of its roots minus the product of the roots.

$$a^3 + b^3 = (a + b)(a^2 - ab + b^2)$$

Like the results of factoring the difference of two cubes, the results of factoring the sum of two cubes is also made up of a binomial factor $(a + b)$ and a trinomial factor $(a^2 - ab + b^2)$.

Notice that the sign between the two cube roots $(a + b)$ is the same as the sign in the problem to be factored $(a^3 + b^3)$. The squares in the trinomial expression are still both positive, but you change the sign of the middle term to minus.

✔ Look at this practical example to get a clearer idea of how to factor the sum of two cubes.

$$1{,}000z^3 + 343$$

The cube root of $1{,}000z^3$ is $10z$, and the cube root of 343 is 7. The product of $10z$ and 7 is $70z$.

$$1{,}000z^3 + 343 = (10z + 7)(100z^2 - 70z + 49)$$

Tinkering with Trinomials and More

You can choose from a total of two methods to factor expressions with three terms, also known as trinomials:

- ✔ Finding the GCF
- ✔ UnFOILing

For more information on both methods, see Chapter 9. Any factoring problem is a matter of recognizing what you have so you know what method to apply. With trinomials, you can use unFOIL if the trinomial is of the form $ax^2 + bx + c$. You can find the GCF if a common factor is available. After checking for both of these situations, if neither fits, then you're done! The trinomial can't be factored.

Basically, you can factor an expression with four, six, eight, or more terms either by finding the GCF or by grouping.

Chapter 9 covers finding the greatest common factor in detail, and grouping polynomials is covered in the next section.

Grouping

The other choice for factoring four or more terms is to try grouping terms to make the new groups factorable. Grouping is first covered in Chapter 9, but this chapter broadens the process to more terms and other types of grouping.

Splitting four terms into two groups of two terms

The most common form of grouping is finding a different common factor in each of the two groups formed from four terms. First, split the four terms down the middle to start forming groups. If this doesn't work, put the terms with something in common in the same group to change the order of the terms. You take the common factor out of each group, separately, and then hope to find a new common factor in the new terms. The new common factor usually results from factoring each separate group. The following example may help you to understand grouping four or more terms:

✔ Factor $8ax + 12ay + 10bx + 15by$.

The first two terms share the common factor 4a, and the second two terms have a common factor of $5b$.

$$8ax + 12ay + 10bx + 15by = 4a\,(2x + 3y) + 5b(2x + 3y)$$

In this case, the grouping resulted in two new terms, each with a factor of $(2x + 3y)$. This new factor is common to both, so the GCF method is going to work.

Take that common factor out of the two new terms and see what you have.

$$4a(2x + 3y) + 5b(2x + 3y) = (4a + 5b)\,(2x + 3y)$$

Done!

Dividing six terms into two or three groups

The next example has six terms. Because 2 and 3 divide 6 evenly, there's the chance that the groups can be two groups of three terms or three groups of two terms each. Sometimes you can do it either way. Sometimes you just have to try until you find the right way. In this case, both ways work.

✔ Factor by dividing the terms into two groups of three.

$$ax^2 + 3ax + 2a + bx^2 + 3bx + 2b$$

The first three terms have a common factor of a, and the second three terms have a common factor of b.

$$a(x^2 + 3x + 2) + b(x^2 + 3x + 2)$$

There are now two groups, each with a common factor of $(x^2 + 3x + 2)$.

$$a(x^2 + 3x + 2) + b(x^2 + 3x + 2) = (x^2 + 3x + 2)(a + b)$$

Notice that the first factor is a quadratic that can be factored with unFOIL.

$$(x^2 + 3x + 2) = (x + 1)(x + 2)$$

$$(x^2 + 3x + 2)(a + b) = (x + 1)(x + 2)(a + b)$$

✔ Grouping the terms two at a time is another way to work this problem. Rearrange the terms, putting the x^2 variables, the x variables, and the numbers together.

$$ax^2 + bx^2 + 3ax + 3bx + 2a + 2b$$

The first two terms have a common factor of x^2, the third and fourth terms have a common factor of $3x$, and the last two terms have a common factor of 2.

$$x^2(a + b) + 3x(a + b) + 2(a + b)$$

Now you have three terms, each with a factor of $(a + b)$. Take the $(a + b)$ out of each term to get:

$$(a + b)(x^2 + 3x + 2) = (a + b)(x + 1)(x + 2)$$

Which way do you like best? You can choose whichever you find easiest and be assured that you'll get the same answer as everyone else.

Uneven grouping

The grouping so far has involved four or six terms divided into equal-size groups. Sometimes four terms can be separated into unequal groupings with three terms in one group and one term in the other. The way to spot these is to look for squares. Of course, you usually don't even look for unequal groupings unless other grouping methods have failed you.

✔ Factor $x^2 + 8x + 16 - y^2$.

This has four terms, but there's no good equal pairing of terms that will give you a set of useful common factors. Another option is to group unevenly. Group the first three terms together because they form a trinomial that can be factored. That leaves the last term by itself.

$$x^2 + 8x + 16 - y^2 = (x^2 + 8x + 16) - y^2$$

Factor the trinomial using unFOIL.

$$(x + 4)^2 - y^2$$

Notice that there are now two terms, and that each is a perfect square.

Using the rule from the "Factoring the difference of two perfect squares" section, earlier in this chapter, $a^2 - b^2 = (a + b)(a - b)$, finish this example:

$$(x + 4)^2 - y^2 = [(x + 4) + y][(x + 4) - y]$$

There's no big advantage to dropping the parentheses inside the brackets, so leave the answer the way it is.

Knowing When to Quit

Factoring is done when no more parts can be factored. If you refer to the listing of ways to factor two, three, or four (or more) terms, then you can check off the options, discard those that don't fit, and stop when none works. After doing one type of factoring, you should then look at the values in parentheses to see if any of them can be factored.

When factoring, determine what type of expression you have — binomial, trinomial, squares, cubes, and so on. This helps you decide what method to use. Keep going, checking inside all parentheses for more factoring opportunities, until you're done.

✔ Factor $4x^4y - 108xy$.

The GCF of the two terms is $4xy$. Factor that out first.

$$4x^4y - 108xy = 4xy(x^3 - 27)$$

The binomial in the parentheses is the difference of two perfect cubes and can be factored using the rule from earlier in this chapter.

$$4xy(x^3 - 27) = 4xy(x - 3)(x^2 + 3x + 9)$$

Even though the last factor, the trinomial, seems to be a candidate for unFOIL, you needn't bother when you get the trinomial from factoring cubes because unFOIL can't factor them. The only thing that may factor them is finding a GCF.

You're finished!

✔ Factor $x^4 - 104x^2 + 400$.

There's no GCF, so the only other option when there are three terms is to unFOIL.

$x^4 = x^2 \times x^2$, and one pair of factors of 400 is 4 and 100; that's the pair that has a sum of 104.

$$x^4 - 104x^2 + 400 = (x^2 - 4)(x^2 - 100)$$

There are now two factors, but each of them is the difference of perfect squares.

$$(x^2 - 4)(x^2 - 100) = (x + 2)(x - 2)(x + 10)(x - 10)$$

You're finished!

✔ Factor $3x^5 - 18x^3 - 81x$.

The GCF of the terms is $3x$.

$$3x^5 - 18x^3 - 81x = 3x(x^4 - 6x^2 - 27)$$

The trinomial can be unFOILed.

$$3x(x^4 - 6x^2 - 27) = 3x(x^2 - 9)(x^2 + 3)$$

The second binomial is the difference of squares.

$$3x(x^2 - 9)(x^2 + 3) = 3x(x - 3)(x + 3)(x^2 + 3)$$

You're finished not only with this problem, but with this chapter!

Chapter 12

Solving Simple Linear Equations

*I*n this chapter, you find all the different ways to solve linear equations with just two terms. Linear means that the highest power of any variable you're solving for is 1. Instead of having just an expression with no equal sign (=) and no relationship to anything else, an equation, which always has an equal sign, makes a statement about whatever is on one side of the equal sign being equal to the value on the other side. In this chapter, instead of dealing with expressions, such as $3x + 2$, I show you how to solve equations, such as $3x + 2 = 11$.

Two-term equations, unlike two-term presidents, are pretty simple, and you can apply the techniques you use on these equations to more complicated equations.

When you use algebra in the real world, more often than not you turn to a formula to help you work through a problem. Fortunately, when it comes to algebraic formulas, you don't have to reinvent the wheel: You can make use of standard, tried-and-true formulas to solve some common, everyday problems.

Solving with Division

One of the most basic methods for solving equations is to divide each side of the equation by the same number. Many formulas and equations include a *coefficient*, or multiplier, with the variable. To get rid of the multiplier and solve the equation, you divide. Look at the following example of how to do this:

Solve for the value of *x* in the equation $20x = 170$.

> **1. Determine the multiplier of the variable and divide both sides by it.**
>
> Because the equation involves multiplying 20 times, undo the multiplication in the equation by doing the opposite of times, which is *divide*.
>
> Divide each side by 20.
>
> $$\frac{20x}{20} = \frac{170}{20}$$
>
> **2. Reduce both sides of the equal sign.**
>
> $$\frac{\cancel{20}x}{\cancel{20}} = \frac{170}{20}$$
>
> $$x = 8.5$$

 Do unto one side of the equation what the other side has had done unto it.

Now try another example to get a better understanding.

If your boss makes five times as much money as you do, and her salary is $200,000, what is your salary? (The bigger puzzle may be why she makes so much!)

Write this puzzle as an equation, letting *x* represent your salary: $5x = 200,000$.

> **1. Determine the multiplier of the variable and divide both sides by it.**
>
> Because the puzzle involves 5 times, undo the multiplication in the puzzle by doing the opposite of multiplication, which is division.

TECHNICAL STUFF

Archimedes — mover and bather

Born about 287 B.C., Archimedes, an inspired mathematician and inventor, devised a pump to raise water from a lower level to a higher level. These pumps were used for irrigation, in ships and mines, and are still used today in some parts of the world.

He also made astronomical instruments and designed tools for the defense of his city during a war. Known for being able to move great weights with simple levers, cogwheels, and pulleys, Archimedes determined the smallest possible cylinder that could contain a sphere

and thus discovered how to calculate the volume of a sphere. The sphere/cylinder diagram was engraved on his tombstone.

A favorite legend has it that as Archimedes lowered himself into a bath, he had a revelation involving how he could determine the purity of a gold object using a similar water-immersion method. He was so excited at the revelation that he jumped out of the tub and ran naked through the streets of the city shouting, "Eureka! Eureka!" (I have found it!)

Divide each side of the equation by 5.

$$\frac{5 \cdot x}{5} = \frac{200,000}{5}$$

$$\frac{\cancel{5} \cdot x}{\cancel{5}} = \frac{200,000}{5}$$

The 5 in the numerator and the 5 in the denominator cancel each other out on the left. On the right,

$$\frac{200,000}{5} = 40,000.$$

2. **Reduce both sides of the equal sign.**

$$x = 40,000$$

The answer to the puzzle is that you make $40,000.

Solving with Multiplication

The opposite operation of multiplication is division. Division was used in the preceding section to solve equations where a number multiplies the variable. The reverse occurs in this section; use multiplication where a number divides the variable.

Look at the following example. Try solving for y in $\frac{y}{11} = -2$.

1. **Determine the value that divides the variable and multiply both sides by it.**

   In this case, 11 is dividing the y, so that's what you multiply by.

   $$11\left(\frac{y}{11}\right) = (-2)(11)$$

2. **Reduce both sides of the equal sign.**

   $$\cancel{11}\left(\frac{y}{\cancel{11}}\right) = -22$$

   $$y = -22$$

Try out this puzzle: A wealthy woman's will dictated that her fortune be divided evenly among her nine cats. Each feline got $500,000, so what was her total fortune before it was split up? (Cats don't pay inheritance tax.)

   Let f represent the amount of her fortune. Then you can write the equation:

   $$\frac{f}{9} = 500,000$$

1. **Determine the value that divides the variable and multiply both sides by it.**

   The fortune divided by 9 gave a share of $500,000.

   In this equation, the fortune was divided. Solve the puzzle by multiplying each side by 9. The opposite of division is multiplication, so multiplication undoes what division did.

2. **Reduce both sides of the equal sign.**

   $$\cancel{9}\left(\frac{f}{\cancel{9}}\right) = 4,500,000$$

   $$f = \$4,500,000$$

   Her fortune was four and a half million dollars. Those are nine very happy kitties.

Solving with Reciprocals

Multiplication and division are opposite operations. Multiplication is undone by division and vice versa, as you've seen in the earlier sections. Another option, though, may work better at times — using the reciprocal or multiplicative inverse of the number that you're trying to "get rid of." Choose this alternative if a fraction is multiplying the variable, such as in

$$\frac{3x}{19} = 12$$

Two numbers are reciprocals if multiplying them together yields a product of 1.

Look at the following examples of reciprocals:

- ✔ 5 and $\frac{1}{5}$ are reciprocals of each other: $5\left(\frac{1}{5}\right) = 1$.

- ✔ $-\frac{3}{7}$ and $-\frac{7}{3}$ are reciprocals: $\left(-\frac{3}{7}\right)\left(-\frac{7}{3}\right) = 1$.

- ✔ The reciprocal of a is $\frac{1}{a}$.

- ✔ The reciprocal of $\frac{1}{b}$ is b.

Solving equations in the fewest possible steps is usually preferable. That's why you can choose to multiply both sides of an equation by $\frac{5}{4}$, the reciprocal of $\frac{4}{5}$, to solve for a in the expression $\frac{4a}{5}$, which can be thought of as $\left(\frac{4}{5}\right)a$.

In the following examples, both sides of the equation are multiplied by the reciprocal of the fraction multiplying the variable.

- ✔ In this example, the variable is multiplied by $\frac{4}{5}$.

$$\frac{4a}{5} = 12$$

Multiply each side by the reciprocal, $\frac{5}{4}$.

$$\frac{5}{4}\left(\frac{4a}{5}\right) = \left(\frac{5}{4}\right) \cdot 12$$

Reduce and simplify.

$$\frac{\cancel{3}}{\cancel{4}}\left(\frac{\cancel{4}a}{\cancel{3}}\right)=\left(\frac{5}{\cancel{4}}\right)\cdot\cancel{12}\ 3$$

$$a=15$$

✔ Solve for $\frac{x}{2}=19$.

$\frac{x}{2}$ is another way of saying $\left(\frac{1}{2}\right)\cdot x$.

So you can solve by multiplying by the reciprocal of $\frac{1}{2}$, which is 2.

$$\frac{\cancel{2}}{1}\left(\frac{1x}{\cancel{2}}\right)=19\left(\frac{2}{1}\right)$$

$$x=38$$

✔ Solve for f: $-f=11$

This is an easy equation to solve, but you may be surprised at how many people get the wrong answer — all because of a little dash in front of a letter. Think of the f as being multiplied by 1. Putting in the 1 gives you a multiplier that you can work with to solve the equation.

What's the reciprocal of –1? It's –1!

$$-f=11$$

$$(-1)(-1f)=11(-1)$$

$$f=-11$$

Setting Up Equations

Solving equations can be fun, especially when the equation has a purpose — to answer a question or solve a problem — and a reality check. This section shows you how to write an equation to answer a question or solve a problem you may have. That's why algebra was developed in the first place — to answer questions and solve problems. Then I discuss whether an answer makes sense or not — doing the reality check.

Changing a written problem into an algebra equation is sort of like translating from one language to another. And the language of algebra has solutions! You need to choose a variable to represent a number in the problem — a number of cats, a number of dimes, and so on. The operations of addition, subtraction, multiplication, and division replace expressions such as more than, fewer than, times as many, and so on. For a complete review of how these operations can be used, see Chapter 1.

The following simple sentence can be easily translated into an algebraic statement: Hugo's 19 books are 3 more than twice as many books as Buck has. The words and expressions to pick up are 19 and 3 more than twice. Let x be the number of books that Buck has. The verb *are* becomes an equal sign (=). *Three more than* is 3 + and *twice* becomes $2x$ because it's twice the number of books. The algebraic equation is $19 = 3 + 2x$.

Now, that wasn't too bad, was it?

Finding a purpose

The following example demonstrates *purpose* (the equation answers a question or solves a problem) and *reality check* (the answer appears to be correct).

A famous rock group called Aftermath sold 130,000 copies of their latest CD. This particular CD cost $16. The equation's purpose is to answer the question: What was the total amount of revenue made from the sale of the CDs?

So, what to do? How to solve this?

Letting r represent the total revenue and using the 130,000 and 16, you can set up an equation several different ways. Find the one that's the correct interpretation — the one that solves the problem.

- ✔ **Choice 1:** Cost of each times total revenue equals number of copies:

$$16 \cdot r = 130{,}000$$

- ✔ **Choice 2:** Total revenue divided by the cost of one item equals the number of items sold:

$$\frac{r}{16} = 130{,}000$$

- ✔ **Choice 3:** Number of copies divided by total revenue equals cost of each:

$$\frac{130{,}000}{r} = 16$$

✔ **Choice 4:** Total revenue divided by number of copies equals cost of each:

$$\frac{r}{130,000} = 16$$

You know that multiplying what something sells for times the number of items sold is how you figure out how much money you make, so Choice 2 or Choice 4 works because each requires multiplying the number sold times the cost of each.

In Choice 2, if the total revenue is divided by the cost of each, then the answer is how many CDs were sold. Multiply 16 times 130,000 to get the total revenue.

$$\frac{r}{16} = 130,000$$

$$16 \cdot \frac{r}{16} = 130,000 \cdot 16$$

$$r = 2,080,000$$

In Choice 4, if the number of CDs sold divides the total revenue, then the answer is how much each CD costs. Multiply 130,000 times 16 to get the total revenue.

$$\frac{r}{130,000} = 16$$

$$130,000 \cdot \frac{r}{130,000} = 16 \cdot 130,000$$

$$r = 2,080,000$$

The total revenue is over two million dollars.

Doing a reality check

No, don't try to do a reality check here — it's way beyond simple reason to make that much money. The following problem, however, offers a good example of how a reality check can spare you.

The number of soccer players participating at a summer soccer camp is 330 — 11 from each club. You're preparing club participation certificates to give to each club captain, so you need to create an equation to answer the question of how many clubs are represented.

To show you that a reality check can save you from making a big error, pretend that you didn't really think this through and solve the problem with the following equation.

The letter *c* represents the number of soccer clubs.

$$\frac{c}{11} = 330$$

You used the variable and the two numbers in the problem. Does it matter what you use where? Will the equation give you a reasonable answer?

Multiply each side by 11 to solve for *c*.

$$11 \cdot \frac{c}{11} = 330 \cdot 11$$

$$\cancel{11} \cdot \frac{c}{\cancel{11}} = 330 \cdot 11$$

$$c = 3,630 \text{ clubs}$$

Now, do a reality check. Does the answer make any sense? The answer may satisfy your equation, but if it doesn't make sense, then the equation could be wrong.

Your answer is 3,630 soccer clubs. You're to prepare 3,630 certificates. You realize that something is wrong because only 330 players are involved. You must have made an error.

A quick look at the equation shows that it should have read:

11 players per club times the number of clubs = total number of players

$$11c = 330$$

Now, solve this.

$$11c = 330$$

Divide each side by 11.

$$\frac{11}{11}c = \frac{330}{11}$$

$$\frac{\cancel{11}}{\cancel{11}}c = \frac{330}{11} \qquad \text{E}$$

$$c = 30 \text{ clubs}$$

That makes much more sense.

You can solve an equation correctly, but that doesn't mean you chose the right equation to solve in the first place. Make sure that your answer makes sense.

Chapter 13

The Ten Most Common Errors

*S*o much algebra is done in the world: Just about everyone who advances beyond elementary school takes an
algebra class, so the sheer number of people who use algebra
means that a large number of errors are made. Forgetting
some of the more obscure rules or confusing one rule with
another is easy to do. But some errors occur because the
error seems to be an easier way to do the problem. Not right,
but easier — the path of least resistance. This usually happens when a rule isn't the same as your natural inclination.
Most algebra rules seem to make sense, so they aren't hard
to remember. Some, though, go against the grain.

The main errors occur while working expanding-type operations: distributing, squaring binomials, breaking up fractions,
or raising to powers. The other big error area is in dealing
with negatives. Watch out for those negative vibes.

Missing Middle Term

A squared binomial has three terms in the answer. The term that gets left out is the middle term: the part you get when multiplying the two outer terms together and the two inner terms together and finding their sum. Often, just the first and last separate terms are squared, and the middle term is just forgotten.

Right: $(a + b)^2 = a^2 + 2ab + b^2$

Wrong: $(a + b)^2 \neq a^2 + b^2$

Go to Chapter 8 for more information on squaring binomials.

Distributing

Distributing a number or a negative sign over two or more terms in a parentheses can cause problems if you forget to distribute the value over every single term in the parentheses. The errors come in when you stop multiplying the terms in the parentheses before you get to the end.

Right: $x - 2(y + z - w) = x - 2y - 2z + 2w$

Wrong: $x - 2(y + 2 - w) \neq x - 2y + z - w$

There's more on distributing in Chapter 8.

Breaking Up Fractions

Splitting a fraction into several smaller pieces is all right as long as each piece has a term from the numerator (top) and the entire bottom (denominator). You can't split up the denominator.

Right: $\dfrac{x + y}{a + b} = \dfrac{x}{a + b} + \dfrac{y}{a + b}$

Wrong: $\dfrac{x + y}{a + b} \neq \dfrac{x}{a} + \dfrac{y}{b}$

Go to Chapter 3 for more on dealing with fractions.

Breaking Up Radicals

If the expression under a radical has values multiplied together or divided, then the radical can be split up into radicals that multiply or divide. You can't split up addition or subtraction, however, under a radical.

Right: $\sqrt{a^2 + b^2} = \sqrt{a^2 + b^2}$

Wrong: $\sqrt{a^2 + b^2} \neq \sqrt{a^2} + \sqrt{b^2}$

For more on radicals, go to Chapter 4.

Order of Operations

The order of operations instructs you to raise the expression to a power before you add or subtract. A negative in front of a term is in the same category as subtracting. It has to be done last. If you want the negative raised to the power, too, then include it in parentheses with the rest of the value.

Right: $-3^2 = -9$

Right: $(-3)^2 = 9$

Wrong: $-3^2 \neq 9$

The order of operations is discussed fully in Chapter 5.

Fractional Exponents

A fractional exponent has the power on the top of the fraction and the root on the bottom. Remember, when writing $\sqrt{x}$ as a term with a fractional exponent, $\sqrt{x} = x^{1/2}$. A fractional exponent indicates that there's a radical involved. The 2 in the fractional exponent is on the bottom — the root always is the bottom number.

Right: $\sqrt[5]{x^3} = x^{3/5}$

Wrong: $\sqrt[5]{x^3} \neq x^{5/3}$

Check out Chapter 4 for more on fractional exponents.

Multiplying Bases Together

When multiplying numbers with exponents and the same base, you add the exponents and leave the base as it is. The bases never get multiplied together.

Right: $2^3 \times 2^4 = 2^7$

Wrong: $2^3 \times 2^4 \neq 4^7$

Go to Chapter 4 for more on multiplying numbers with exponents and the same base.

A Power to a Power

To raise a value that has a power to another power, multiply the exponents to raise the whole term to another power. Don't raise the exponent itself to a power — it's the base that's being raised, not the exponent.

Right: $(x^2)^4 = x^8$

Wrong: $(x^2)^4 \neq x^{16}$

Chapter 4 is the place to go for more on powers.

Reducing

When reducing fractions with a numerator that has more than one term separated by addition or subtraction, whatever you're reducing the fraction by has to divide every single term evenly in both the numerator and denominator.

Right: $\dfrac{(4+6x)}{4} = \dfrac{(2+3x)}{2}$

Wrong: $\dfrac{(4+6x)}{4} \neq \dfrac{(2+6x)}{2}$

Go to Chapter 3 if you want more information on fractions.

Negative Exponents

When changing fractions to expressions with negative exponents, give every single factor in the denominator a negative exponent.

Right: $\dfrac{1}{2ab^2} = 2^{-1}a^{-1}b^{-2}$

Wrong: $\dfrac{1}{2ab^2} \neq 2a^{-1}b^{-2}$

There's more on negative exponents in Chapter 4.

Index

Notes

Notes